The Troubled Mind

A PSYCHIATRIC STUDY OF
SUCCESS AND FAILURE IN
HUMAN ADAPTATION

by

BEULAH CHAMBERLAIN BOSSELMAN, M.D.
CLINICAL ASSOCIATE PROFESSOR OF PSYCHIATRY
UNIVERSITY OF ILLINOIS MEDICAL SCHOOL

THE RONALD PRESS COMPANY · NEW YORK

Copyright, 1953, by
THE RONALD PRESS COMPANY

All Rights Reserved

The text of this publication or any part
thereof may not be reproduced in any
manner whatsoever without permission in
writing from the publisher.

Library of Congress Catalog Card Number: 53-10380

PRINTED IN THE UNITED STATES OF AMERICA

Preface

THE boundaries of normal and abnormal ways of human adaptation are not clearly defined. Success and failure are relative concepts, varying according to the individual's expectations of himself and the demands which society makes upon him. It is obvious, however, that the person who struggles with a sense of defeat finds himself reacting in ways that often become progressively more unrealistic and inefficient. His disorganized attempts at adaptation then become "symptoms," which vary from slight, casually accepted disturbances of function to the bizarre manifestations of neuroses and psychoses. In this troubled state he asks for help—help that would have been more effective given earlier, before his progressive pattern of maladjustment was so firmly established. It is this help that parents with their children, teachers with their students, clergymen with their parishioners, and physicians with their patients can give through a greater understanding of the motivations and the difficulties that determine human behavior.

This book begins with a concise account of the processes of development from infancy through old age, with particular attention to the specific problems that must be solved at each age level if one is to reach a satisfactory state of adult adaptation. The patterns of defeat which have their extreme representation in neuroses and psychoses are then described and interpreted. Finally, suggestions are offered for improvement of mental health, taking into account the contribution of those groups whose work is closely concerned with human relationships.

The tendency in our present-day culture is toward a more frank and tolerant interpretation of mental illness. We no longer think of the emotionally disturbed person as possessed of devils. However, an attitude of mystery and embarrassment about these conditions still, to some extent, persists. This discourages the scientific-humanitarian approach that is necessary for diagnosis, treatment, and prevention. The hope of present-day psychiatry is that of establishing the more constructive viewpoint.

I am grateful to Dr. Francis J. Gerty, Professor and Head of the Department of Psychiatry of the University of Illinois Medical School, for the wide horizons which he envisions in the field of psychiatric teaching. Dr. Gerty's encouragement of the points of view of this book and his helpfulness in reading and constructively criticizing the manuscript have been of much value to me. My thanks go also to Mrs. Ada Corson for her careful preparation of the manuscript.

BEULAH CHAMBERLAIN BOSSELMAN

Chicago, Illinois
July, 1953

Contents

PART I

The Problem of Adaptation

CHAPTER		PAGE
1	INFANCY: The Attainment of Self-Realization	3
2	EARLY CHILDHOOD: Love and Hate in Close Interpersonal Relationships	12
3	LATER CHILDHOOD: Adaptation Within the Peer Group	20
4	ADOLESCENCE: Transition into Maturity	28
5	MATURITY: Adequacy and Overflow	36
6	INVOLUTION AND OLD AGE: The Problem of Self-Acceptance	45
7	CHARACTER FORMATION	52

PART II

Adaptations That Fail

8	ADAPTATIONS UNREALISTIC AND INEFFICIENT: Neurosis	73
9	ADAPTATION BY DISTORTION AND DENIAL: Psychosis	110

PART III

The Problem of Treatment

10	AGENCIES OF HEALTH	153
	SUGGESTIONS FOR FURTHER READING	193
	INDEX	201

PART I

The Problem of Adaptation

chapter 1

INFANCY: The Attainment of Self-Realization

> The baby, assailed by eyes, ears, nose, skin and entrails all at once, feels it all as one great, blooming, buzzing confusion.
> —William James: *Principles of Psychology*

IF WE examine with perspective the problems of adaptation with which every human being must deal in his journey from infancy to old age, we find that these problems group themselves in a relatively distinct and progressive way.

The first adaptation concerns the need of the infant to define himself as separate from the rest of the world, as significant within limitations. As a young child he must establish satisfactory relationships within his family and later within his social group. This accomplished, the youth is expected to make a transition into the self-sufficiency of maturity and as an adult to deal with the responsibilities involved. Finally, as his path slopes downward the man or woman must find peace within himself; he must accept, stoically or by faith, his place in the universe.

On the basis of these fundamental adaptive tasks, we

may define the developmental periods of life, recognizing the fact that within each period the essential problems must be solved lest cumulative difficulties develop. If the child of five has not mastered his second-year adaptations, he finds the demands of the fifth year confusing and may withdraw from them, clinging to earlier patterns. The young boy and girl who have not built a good foundation in interpersonal relationships through their earlier experiences with parents and playmates are not ready to cope with adolescence. Maturity implies a capacity for giving which can be achieved only after a satisfactory emancipation has been accomplished in adolescence. And the breadth and depth of outlook which alone can sustain in the later years are the product of integrations made in the period of maturity.

The first age of man, that of infancy, can be understood only on the basis of observation and assumption. The universal experiences of infancy are not retained for later reminiscent analysis. Only an occasional vague fragment before the age of three remains accessible to recall.

However, although the experiences of infancy do not persist in memory, they are of great significance in determining the kind of person who emerges from this "blooming, buzzing confusion" into the more self-aware years. They serve as an introduction to the physical and social realities. In these experiences the infant must accomplish his first adaptive task: that of defining himself as apart from the external world, a significant, self-expressive individual, yet bound and limited by that which lies outside himself.

As we observe the newly born person we see him motivated, like all simple organisms, by comfort-seeking. His behavior is directed toward achieving freedom from disturbing external stimuli and inner tensions. He wants to be fed, warm, and undisturbed. His life within the womb had a kind of omnipotence in that his environment there was admirably fitted for serving his needs. His postnatal environment, however wisely presented, subjects him to the discomforts, restraints, and denials which initiate adaptive responses and make it necessary that he become aware of his limitations as an individual. There is no turning back in the normal developmental process. Having sensed his boundaries, he can never again return to a state of self-absorbed unconcern.

The young infant's random behavior serves him for testing reality. Muscular movements disclose barriers so that he becomes aware of physical restrictions. He is hungry and cries for food. If food is not immediately available he again must deal with a restriction which, in this case, begins to be related to another person. Not only is he enmeshed in the physical facts of his world, but also he must deal with the behavior directed toward him by his caretakers.

Already, in these earliest months, patterns of adaptation emerge. The well-adjusted baby shows a good balance between aggressive demand and relaxed conformity to schedule. Less satisfactory is the behavior of the restless, overactive, fretful infant, or on the other hand the apathetic, nonresponsive one.

These earliest reactions are, no doubt, to some extent constitutionally determined. Parents commonly remark about the extreme differences in response of children reared under apparently like circumstances. The similarity of behavior of identical twins as contrasted with fraternal twins also emphasizes the constitutional factor. Anyone's intelligence, as well as his less clearly defined heritage of energy and homeostasis (maintenance of a steady state of functioning), influences the nature of his adaptive patterns.

It is obvious, however, that good adaptation is not simply and exclusively correlated with good native endowment. Constitution provides tools with which one can function, and tools delimit accomplishment in a quantitative way. But the skill with which they are used depends on experience. It is experience which determines the quality, and particularly the social quality, of the emerging behavior which we see in the infant. Intellect may be realistically applied, or drained off in antisocial or neurotic tendencies. The qualitative determination depends on the nature of the concepts which everyone at birth begins to form in the physical and social interactions which constitute his experience.

It is impossible to separate sharply the roles of heredity and environment, and controversy on this subject seems to create a futile and misleading dichotomy. The important issue is the fact that *a human being, infant or adult, must be equipped at any time to deal efficiently with the environmental problems presented at that time*. In so far as the equipment is the product of heredity there is little that can be done about the problem but, in so far as it is the result of previous experience, it becomes a modifiable balance. It is, therefore, most important for parents in dealing with children never to exceed or underestimate their capacity for adaptation at any developmental stage. In other words, reality should be presented to the child in "correct doses": sufficient to encourage growth but not so excessive as to intimidate or discourage the child. If parents are wise, they will not frantically attempt to perpetuate a sense of omnipotence by attending to their child's slightest demand. They will, on the other hand, avoid creating excessive tensions which provide the foundations for discouraged and fretful attitudes.

There has been a good deal of vacillation in the stand taken by mothers and their advisors on the issue of regimentation versus permissiveness in child rearing. At present there is a healthy trend away from rigid rules for regulation of feeding and toilet training. Emphasis is on following the child's own needs rather than on imposing a regime shaped only to the convenience of the adults concerned. The modern method seems more conducive to relaxed and confident attitudes. It seems reasonable that children handled in this way will conceive of the external world as a relatively generous and considerate place. However, even liberal rules can be rigidly applied, and if parents become too greatly concerned lest they restrict their children in any way, they may fail to give their child the necessary preparation for the "larger doses" of reality which he will meet outside the protective parental environment.

The rules for child care imposed by dictum are not as helpful as they might be because actually no rule is as important as the way in which it is applied. The infant in an atmosphere of love and joyful acceptance will react without great damage to errors in management; but if the *feeling* is wrong, he is vulnerable to mismanagement and may in early months develop characteristic anxieties and dissatisfactions which sometimes persist throughout his life.

The good parent will sense the importance both of gratifying the infant and of giving him a growing sense of cooperation in a well-regulated world. Thus the child may avoid the extremes of an overintimidated, repressed docility and of a restless, anxious impulsiveness.

When Shakespeare in one of his infrequent references to the infant was satisfied to describe him as "mewling and puking in the nurse's arms," he suggested the disregard for the significance of this period of life which has prevailed in many periods of human history. It is probably a relatively unique viewpoint, historically, which regards the early months of life as dynamic and of far-reaching consequence for later years. Our more prevalent present acceptance of this viewpoint is the result of a great deal of emphasis on the individual in a democratic social organization, plus the accumulating evidence of psychological studies.

One of the most interesting investigations of the reactions of young infants to their environments is that of Dr. Renee Spitz.* Dr. Spitz observed two groups of illegitimate babies reared in two institutions of similar excellent physical setup but differing in that the children in one were cared for by their mothers, whereas in the other they never saw their mothers and received only the most impersonal, routine care of nurses. For the first six months, the infants' developmental progress showed no appreciable difference in the two institutions and as compared with a control group of babies in their homes. After the sixth month, however, the infants cared for by their mothers progressed with normal rapidity, whereas those in the other institution showed a marked retardation in development and exhibited much regressive, apathetic, and antisocial behavior. Surprisingly enough, the "unloved" infants also showed a very much higher death rate than did those receiving a mother's care, in spite of an equal quality in their medical and nursing supervision.

* Renee Spitz, "Hospitalism," in *Psychoanalytic Study of the Child* (New York: International Universities Press, Inc., 1945), Vol. I.

These studies of Dr. Spitz are confirmed by the observations of experienced pediatricians * as to the close relationship between the emotional life of the infant and his physical and personality development.

During the period from six months to two years, the child's interpersonal contacts are expressed largely in relation to: first, his feeding and second, his training in cleanliness and regularity, which centers about his elimination. The parents' method of handling these matters is important, and even more important is the rapport between parent and child—the emotional atmosphere which affects to a large extent the child's cooperation.

So-called feeding problems in the early years are very common in our culture, probably because emphasis on correct nutrition and, until very recently, upon a very rigid feeding regime has made this function an issue between mother and child. The child, feeling forced and cajoled, can make use of this issue as an opportunity for resisting authority. The dependent little creature has, after all, few ways of self-assertion in a world of adults who slowly but surely are molding him to their will. In the same way, training in habits of elimination becomes the focus point of much rebellious feeling. Here the problem is more complicated in that not only conformity in routine but also conformity of attitude is demanded. A function and a body product are associated with ideas of dirtiness and badness. The child who soils is likely to be labeled as naughty, whereas the one who doesn't eat well gets increased attention and concern. In either case the function becomes, as we have seen, a social issue.

* Benjamin Spock, *Baby and Child Care* (New York: Pocket Books, Inc., 1946). M. J. Senn, *Problems of Early Infancy* (New York: J. Macy, Jr. Foundation, 1947). Arnold Gesell et al., *Infant and Child in the Culture of Today* (New York: Harper & Bros., 1943).

We shall observe later that the character traits which emerge in early childhood are related to the experiences with which the child is emotionally concerned at the time. If the regulation of his eating and elimination becomes associated with much feeling, becomes representative of his interpersonal relationships, then his emergent character traits reflect these attitudes in ways that may be unfavorable.

A sense of oral frustration in infancy may result from insufficient food or from a too rigid or anxious presentation of food. It may indicate a lack of warm, secure personal contact with the mother (or her substitute) who presents the food; the resulting sense of frustration may make the drive toward oral incorporation overly important. It may persist specifically in such tendencies as that of overeating or of developing food fads. Even more serious is its diffusion from specific meaning into a generally "greedy" attitude which becomes a fixed characteristic. The strongly dependent, demanding adult with insatiable needs for love and reassurance may be continuing to demand, in a way more infantile than he realizes, the generous gifts of a mother.

Likewise, the conflicts about conformity and cleanliness which are aroused by toilet training may persist specifically in such habits as constipation and excessive anxiety about elimination, or they too may spread out into general attitudes. The overly trained child may tend to become the excessively neat, exact, compulsive person whose rigid perfectionism covers a basically hostile feeling; or, in contrast, he may tend in the direction of overt rebellion against the strict training and may continue throughout life to express this rebellion in relation to authority of any kind. In such ways do the forgotten or only vaguely remembered experiences of infancy shape the persistent attitudes of the adult.

Even in the best of circumstances, the adaptations of the

first life period are obviously not solved once and for all by the end of the child's second or third year. By this time, however, he should have established a workable and realistic balance between self-assertion and conformity. This will serve him well as he goes on into the more complicated personal entanglements of the next period.

chapter 2

EARLY CHILDHOOD: Love and Hate in Close Interpersonal Relationships

> Now 'tis the Spring, and weeds are shallow-rooted;
> Suffer them now and they'll outgrow the garden.
> —William Shakespeare: *King Henry* VI

JUST as the adaptive problems of infancy are never abruptly solved but are carried over into the succeeding periods of life, so do the problems of early childhood have their beginnings in infancy.

The baby begins to be aware of people, though at first their personalities seem to have little specificity to him. He reacts favorably to familiar figures which comfort and entertain him and he may at times react negatively to strangers, but he shows little evidence of specific attachments, though fond mothers feel otherwise.

Gradually, as his interest crystallizes and focuses on the individuals about him, he does begin to react to them in more specific ways. During the period from the time a child begins to crawl up to the time he is ready for school he vacillates between his dependence on his parents (or their substitutes) and his attempts at independent activity.

Periods of shyness alternate with exhibitionism, curiosity with clinging, negativeness with effusive affection. But whether he rebels or clings to them during these years, the child's parents are very important to him. With them and to a lesser degree with his brothers and sisters, he begins to act out his potentialities for love and hostility. The balance which he achieves determines to a large degree the relative importance of one or the other of these powerful feelings in all his later personal relationships.

The need and capacity for love are manifested so early and with such constancy as to be considered innate human characteristics. They are, to be sure, first shown indiscriminately and in close relationship to the comfort-seeking reactions of the infant. The mother's breast or the soft toy alike give rise to responses of pleasure. Later, these pleasure responses become more selectively related to human love objects and they persist in situations where the loved one is not immediately concerned with the needs of the child.

This is an important distinction, for it marks the passing of infantile narcissism (self-love) and the beginning of capacity for interpersonal rapport. When the young child spontaneously offers his toy to a playmate or weeps over his hurt dog he is establishing favorable patterns of group living. Such behavior cannot be forced upon him. The child who is cajoled into being "good" acts artificially and often with concealed resentment. He must learn consideration of others by example, not by rule. His interest in other persons integrates him within his family, makes him a unit functioning within a larger unit. He still makes demands on parents and siblings but is at the same time affected by their happiness or distress, and this leads to a complicated web of interrelationships.

Just as the tendency to express love is inborn, so obviously is the capacity for hate. This emotion appears, however, as a negative rather than a positive expression, not having the quality of instinctual striving which is characteristic of love, but rather manifested as a defensive reaction against frustration.

Such responses in infancy are of the nature of angry outbursts and struggles against restriction and denial. Only after the child has become aware of people as individuals and has attached specific significance to them is he capable of the person-directed feeling which in its extreme manifestations we call hatred, and in its more diffuse and transitory expressions we call hostility.

The negative emotions are early and easily aroused in the process of living because of the wide discrepancy between spontaneous, self-centered attempts to achieve gratification and the usual denials which are imposed on these activities. Hence even though the early personal relationships of a child are good ones, he is subject to frustration and he will project his anger in hostile reactions which become interwoven with his affectionate, dependent attitudes to produce the characteristic ambivalence of the parent-child relationship. Among siblings, who are essentially rivals, the feelings are even more negative, and strongly competitive reactions are usually the rule here.

Ambivalence is a state of having contrasting feelings toward the same object. One at the same time loves and hates a person close to him. This causes a good deal of conflict, especially if both feelings are strong ones. We shall later see these ambivalent conflicts as the source of many serious psychiatric problems. No one can function entirely without hostility; obviously however, it is extremely important that a good balance be achieved, lest the socially and individually constructive attitudes based on love be too largely replaced by the inhibiting and destructive expressions of hatred. The nature of this balance depends to a very large extent on the close interpersonal relationships of the preschool years.

By the time he is three or four years old, the child has become conscious of himself not only as an individual but also as a girl or a boy. He is interested in and curious about his sexual organs and those of other children. Masturbation and sex play indicate this, as does an active verbal quest for information. Concepts of masculinity and femininity emerge, partly no doubt the result of cultural emphasis on these distinctions, but not exclusively for this reason. To a variable degree, "boyishness" and "girlishness" appear as apparently spontaneous character traits.

In association with his sexual self-awareness, the child now begins to show some more specific attitudes toward his parents. In the prevalent family pattern of our culture, infants of both sexes have a tendency to form the first close and most possessive relationship with the mother (or her substitute), who is the giver of food and is in intimate personal contact. This preference usually continues up to the time of beginning awareness of the parents' separate identities as mother and father, and the child's own concurrent identification of himself as boy or girl. Then there gradually becomes manifested a more intensely emotional fixation on the parent of the opposite sex. This pattern is so characteristic as to indicate a biological trend. It may, however, be distorted in individual cases by parental attitudes. The boy of three to six assumes toward his mother an affectionately possessive air of variable intensity. The little girl relates likewise to her father. This creates a family triangle in which the parent of the same sex becomes a rival for the parent of opposite sex. This situation may arouse a good deal of anxiety because of the child's dependence on the good will of both parents and his obvious inability to compete. The rivalry also involves the brothers and sisters with whom he must share the favored parent's love.

The family love relationships which the child establishes in his first five or six years affect to a large extent the concepts of himself which persist throughout life. In particular, the anxiety and guilt aroused by the erotic nature of the attachments often provide the basis for such manifestations as excessive shyness, attitudes of inferiority, and lack of self-confidence. In the boy these conflicts tend to focus on his sexuality, expressing themselves in castration anxiety which, if unfavorably handled, may remain with him into adult life. This anxiety expresses in its origin the little boy's sense of vulnerability in relation to the more powerful father as a rival for the mother, but it may continue less specifically in his character structure as a feeling of inability to compete as a man among men. The girl may develop similar fears concerning her lack of a penis, particularly if she is given the idea that boys belong to the favored sex. If her attachment to her father stimulates strong rivalries with the mother she is apprehensive lest she lose the mother's love, and may overcompensate for this by a clinging dependence on the mother which continues as a handicapping feature of her adult personality.

Fortunately, in most cases these disturbing conflicts of the child tend to resolve themselves, as do his other problems of maturation. The boy and girl establish for themselves their places in the family. The boy's recognition of mutual interests and attitudes with the father, and the girl's with the mother, favor an identification with the parent of the same sex. In this identification the child's jealousy is overcome and his competitive clinging to the favored parent gives way to a more relaxed sense of family "togetherness." At the same time the boy or girl is beginning to relate himself to the larger group, substituting wider social interests for the clinging dependencies of childhood, and this favors resolution of the conflict.

However, the situation is by no means always resolved in this ideal manner. Many circumstances may interfere. Children lacking one or both parents attempt with varying success to find substitutive objects for their emotional needs. More frequently difficulty results not from lack of a parent figure, but from defects in the mother or father which make a good relationship difficult. Extreme domination or overprotection may bind the child. Disregard, abuse, or marked indifference may repel him. An emotionally deprived parent who uses the child as an object for his (more often, her) own love needs makes maturation difficult.

The position of the child among his siblings is often an important determinant of his attitudes. Each family group has its individual pattern of interrelationships, so generalities are of limited significance; however, it is frequently observed that an oldest child develops a strong sense of responsibility, especially if the parents tend to share problems with him. The youngest child may be encouraged in dependency by the mother who wants to hold on to her baby; the middle child, with a favored older sibling and a pampered younger one on either side, may easily feel a lack of significance in his family position. The only child is spared these problems; his difficulties are those of too close involvement with the parents and lack of experience in a competitive give-and-take situation.

The relative abilities of children influence superiority-inferiority attitudes within the group. A child of average intelligence who would feel adequate in a family of comparable ability is inclined to strong doubts about himself if he must compete with more brilliant siblings. Similarly, the daughter whose plain appearance contrasts with the beauty of mother or sister may be seriously handicapped by lack of confidence in herself as an acceptable female.

Many factors influence parental attitudes to bring about favoritism among children or diverse attitudes toward them. It is commonly observed that parents are more strict with the older children, or more anxious about them, gradually relaxing this tension and allowing greater freedom to the younger members of the family. A child born at a time of poverty or domestic strife finds the emotional atmosphere different from that experienced by a sibling born at a more auspicious time. Furthermore, projections * of feeling on the part of a parent may determine the quality of a parent-child relationship. Sometimes a father who is aggrieved by the lack of a son regards his daughters with disappointment, thus giving them a sense of rejection which may become the foundation for maladjustment. Similarly, much harm may be done to a boy if his mother discourages his masculine, aggressive characteristics.

Marital discord is of course always a fertile source of difficulty for children. The pernicious attempts of some parents to use the one child against another result in great confusion and anxiety, as likewise does rejection of a child who is identified with a hated mate.

Within this often chaotic melee which is the family, the young individual strives to establish a kind of stability.

---

* Projection: attributing one's own attitudes or difficulties to another person.

Attitudes develop in him that reflect his experience. If this experience favors a warm sense of being accepted and a willingness to live cooperatively, it has prepared the child for participation in the larger group. He goes on then into the broader and less intense problems of integration among his peers.*

* Peer: "One who ranks with another in endowment or other qualifications" (Webster). Here used to indicate others of the same age group.

chapter 3

LATER CHILDHOOD:
Adaptation Within the Peer Group

> The boy's will is the wind's will
> And the thoughts of youth are long, long thoughts.
> —H. W. Longfellow: *My Lost Youth*

THE CHILDHOOD years which lie approximately between the time of entering school and the time of beginning adolescence are years which should be relatively free of conflict regarding basic personal relationships. The intense feelings of love and hate which earlier were attached to parents have passed over into a more realistic acceptance by the child of his place within the family. This should imply an awareness of being loved, protected, and understood, and at the same time an awareness of the meaning of cooperative behavior within an intimate group.

A hard-and-fast division between developmental periods does not, of course, apply here any more than it did between the periods of infancy and early childhood. Some children have experience in dealing with their peers in nursery school and play groups from the time they are able to toddle. Others have no participation of this kind up to the time they enter school. The former children have an initial advantage in techniques of approach to a group. However, such an advantage is probably not as important as it might seem, because the very young child is biologically not ready to make much progress with larger group adaptations. Therefore the three-year-old's mastery of the art of getting along with other children may be rather a superficial thing without much relationship to the group integration which he achieves in the next developmental period.

The present popularity of nursery schools does not necessarily indicate their unqualified desirability. For some parents they are made valuable by circumstances; for others they are frankly welcomed as offering temporary relief from the care of the child. Many modern parents mistakenly tend to regard them as necessary institutions contributing to good socialization of the child. Whether the nursery school will be of benefit or harm depends upon the wisdom with which it is administered, and also upon the child's own interpretation of his presence there. This poses questions which can be satisfactorily answered only by evaluation of each individual situation. In any case it is important to recognize that the essential purpose of nursery school is for the supplementing of parental care and not for teaching rules of group adaptation.

We may say that a child approaches gradually the problem of establishing himself in his peer group. The age at which he is ready to deal efficiently with this problem is determined largely by his success at arriving at satisfactory relationships with his parents and, to a much lesser degree, by his opportunities for preschool contacts with other children. His most fundamental attitudes about himself and his acceptance of the world about him have already been formulated. It now remains to be seen whether or not these attitudes can serve him well outside the small area of his own home.

We have observed that methods of child care in the home are not as important as is the atmosphere of feeling in which these methods function. This observation carries over also to the situation of the child within his peer group. If he has established a sense of basically good feelings with his parents, he can tolerate better the impacts of critical or hostile attitudes outside the home. Unfortunate indeed is the boy or girl whose earlier experiences have given him a deep sense of rejection and distrust and who finds these attitudes reinforced by lack of acceptance among his peers. Such a circumstance leads into a vicious circle of maladaptation. The rejection of the group intensifies the child's distrust and hostility, which in turn are expressed in withdrawn or angry behavior; this of course, is conducive to further rejection. On the other hand, favorable acceptance by his peers may reassure the unhappy, insecure child so that in achieving a sense of group solidarity he may overcome, more or less, the destructive features of poor family relationships.

Acceptance or rejection of a child by his peers is an erratic and uncharitable phenomenon conditioned by many factors, and often vacillating in an apparently whimsical way. It depends somewhat, of course, on the prevalent attitudes of the group. Children in a community which is strongly cognizant of the needs of children and offers them opportunities for adequate self-expression in work and play will be likely to be relatively friendly and tolerant of each other. In a dilapidated community, the children's attitudes will tend to reflect the belligerence and overt aggression of the cultural tradition.

Even more important to the individual child, however, is his capacity to fit into the group whatever its character may be. The "outsider" will meet with more brutal treatment among aggressive, poorly socialized children, but he will be unhappy in any community. No quality, however outstanding, is so important to a child of this age as the quality of not being different. Human beings at this early age begin to compensate for weakness by banding together for attack on the minority.

The particular kinds of conditions which make a child likely to be rejected by a group are of wide variety and do not always seem logical. Being a member of a racial or religious minority is often a cause for being ostracized; this may vacillate from time to time, depending on the hostilities of the members, and in relatively tolerant groups it can be forgotten if the child from the minority group proves himself to be acceptable in other ways. Physical handicaps are reacted to with curiosity and often with rejection; but here too, in otherwise favorable circumstances, the handicapped child may in time be accepted and even protected by the group. Children who are by endowment outstandingly different are unfortunate if they must be moved about a great deal. If they remain in one community they become established, taken for granted, and placed according to their capacities. Physical handicap covers many deviations, often minor, which nevertheless may set a child apart. Obesity, extreme tallness, strabismus (cross eyes), stammering or lisping speech, and the like may become the target for ridicule and make good group integration difficult.

Boys and girls of this age, aware as they are of their sexual differences, are critical of deviations from the norm of girlish and boyish behavior. The criticism is much more devastating when applied to the "sissy" boy than when applied to the "tomboy" girl. This difference in the critical attitudes probably indicates not so much a cultural glorification of masculinity (though this may contribute) as it does the importance of independent and aggressive attitudes in this age group. The girl may join the boy in his active, competitive games and even merit admiration if she is successful, but the boy who prefers the quieter pursuits of the girls is looked upon with contempt as a weakling. The boy who is labeled a sissy is harmed not only in his position within the group, but deeply in his own self esteem as well. It is another instance of the vicious circle. The sissy is a boy who in his earliest years has not been able satisfactorily to identify himself as a male, the failure being due in whole or in part to poor relationships with his parents and siblings. This sense of inadequacy expresses itself in withdrawal from aggressive activity, by which he earns the scorn of his male peers, thus adding to his original insecurity. The tomboy may likewise have difficulties in feminine identification which are not so significant during this roustabout period but often become evident in adolescence.

For acceptance by his peers it is not sufficient that the child himself be free of marked deviations from his group, but he is also responsible for the defects of his family in this regard. To begin with, it is important that he *have* a family. The orphan or half-orphan may be looked upon somewhat askance, the state of being adopted may be used at times as a reason for rejection, and known illegitimacy is an almost intolerable burden to bear. Parents may have serious character faults, but if they do not become the subject of community gossip their children will not be taunted with their deficiencies. The child whose parent is a known drunkard, a ne'er-do-well, or who is involved in unpleasant publicity, may have these circumstances used against him.

There is much too little understanding among parents of the importance to the child of being able to fit into his group without marked deviations. This consideration should be taken into account in the question of where to live. Surely it is most unwise, for example, to subject a Jewish child to an environment of anti-Semitic children because the business interests of the father make such a placement convenient. Adults in a minority group may be able to deal with irrational prejudices, but it is too much to expect of children. Also, parents who prefer to protest publicly against established traditions in a way that sets the family apart in a community may create much confusion for their children, who find themselves torn between family loyalties and resentment that the parents subject them to the attack of the group. To adults rebellion may be worth the sacrifices it involves, but children should not be expected to suffer for causes which they cannot comprehend.

One outstanding quality of good parenthood is the ability to see the child's point of view: to understand that certain circumstances are significant to the child even though they seem trifling to the adult. This understanding enables the parent to have a genuine interest in the child's work and play activities. The demands and rebellions of the child can then be more satisfactorily handled because a wise distinction can be made between those which indicate a real need and those which are mere expressions of irritability. For example, a child's insistence on dressing exactly according to the fashion of the group may seem at times unreasonable, but to thwart him in this demand is to expose him to painful ridicule. The too-well-dressed boy or the girl who must wear her dresses a few inches longer or shorter than the prevailing mode is bearing an unnecessary handicap. It is another illustration of the fact that although slavish conformity is logically not warranted the young child is in no position to defy it.

During this period of group adaptation the child's sexual problems should theoretically be quiescent. The intense curiosity of his earlier years, the preoccupation with his body structure and with his sensations, should have by now become less important to him. He should also by now, as has been indicated, have resolved his possessive, competitive strivings for his parents. In most cases this equilibrium has been fairly well attained. There is, however, obviously no sudden and complete cessation of sexual interest, and a good deal of sex play of a casual sort persists. It may be observed between children of the same sex and those of opposite sex rather indiscriminately. Masturbation is less common than in early childhood and adolescence, but it is by no means abnormal.

The well-adjusted child in later childhood will, in other words, not be very much concerned with his sexual activities, though they will manifest themselves from time to time; excessive interest indicates unsatisfactory experiences in the earlier developmental period. Infantilizing or too emotional attitudes on the part of the parents, or an extremely repressive disciplining of sexual curiosity, tends to encourage such persistence. Failure to adjust in the peer group also may favor a regression to earlier preoccupation with sexual feelings. If this is expressed in inordinate masturbation it creates in the child a sense of guilt which is a poor preparation for adolescence. It is, therefore, extremely important that parents and teachers who recognize the persistence of sexual conflict should try to understand and guide the child, rather than subject him to a kind of scornful criticism which greatly intensifies his guilt.

The child emerging from the period of peer group adaptation into adolescence should have learned the lessons of give and take. He should feel that he *belongs* in the group, as earlier he *belonged* in the family. If feelings of isolation persist, if he has retreated away from group adaptation to the protection of his parents, or to absorption in his own fantasies, he is an unhappy child who needs the help of better parental understanding. This help should, if possible, be extended to him before he enters the stormier period ahead when his rebellion makes it difficult for his parents, or any adults, to reach him.*

* See Erik H. Erickson, *Childhood and Society* (New York: W. W Norton & Co., Inc., 1952).

chapter 4

ADOLESCENCE: Transition into Maturity

> Henceforth I ask not good fortune,
>   I myself am good fortune;
> Henceforth I whimper no more,
>   Postpone no more, need nothing—
> Strong and content I travel the open road.
> —Walt Whitman: *Song of the Open Road*

T<small>HE YEARS</small> between approximately thirteen and twenty, those of adolescence, are generally looked upon as constituting a critical and stressful period of life. At this time the relatively impersonal group relationships of the previous period have superimposed on them more intense competitive feelings resulting from increased sexual drives. These intensified feelings bring about in the adolescent a sense of individuality and a striving toward maturity which make it necessary for him to break his close bonds with parents and to establish his own patterns of living. His problem is, therefore, a twofold one. First, he must attain self-confidence and social acceptance of himself as no longer identified with his parents but motivated by his own mores. Second, he must integrate in an acceptable and satisfying way the strong sexual feelings which often, both because of individual experiences and of general cultural attitude, have been regarded with some degree of shame and confusion.

In the adolescent period it is again obvious that difficulties arise on the basis of unfavorable experiences of previous years. This is a testing time which determines the efficacy of established attitudes. The adolescent must build on what he has. There is little that parents can do directly at this time to help him. They can do so indirectly, by dealing with his rebellion in a tolerant and understanding way, but if they attempt to take an active part in solving his problems they will meet with rejection and withdrawal. This is the way it must be. Now or never the young person must assure himself of his self-reliance. The parents will of course "stand by" and at times may have to impose their more mature judgment even at the expense of antagonizing their child, but if the relationship is good these experiences will be relatively infrequent.

The adolescent revolt indeed creates much confusion for parents, even for those who have reared their children with wisdom and consideration. The child's rather sudden change from an attitude of idealization to one of detached criticism demands of the parents much flexibility. The mother and father have not changed; they still love their child and enjoy sharing his interests, so that his withdrawal into his own world away from the previously shared experiences is not easy to accept. Some parents in anger attempt to force control. This results in the atmosphere of conflict so familiar in the home of the adolescent. Others equally futilely try to hold the son or daughter by being "chummy" after the child's own patterns. Mother dresses like daughter, tries to talk her jargon and share her experiences. Father tries to "pal around" with a son who now regards such activities as embarrassing both to his father and to himself.

The wise parents will accept the inevitable, hoping that they have helped their children to build the kind of foundations in good interpersonal relationships which will serve them well as they leave the protective home atmosphere, and knowing that once independence is established their sons and daughters will again dare to be relaxed and affectionate with them.

For the adolescent himself this is a time of extremes of pleasure or pain. The well-adjusted human being of this age is on top of the world. Physically and mentally he is at the height of development: strong, resilient, alert. His feeling-capacities for enjoyment of life are at their peak. His environment is challenging, mysterious, full of new adventure. His sexuality stirs him with sensuous and romantic ecstasy and makes him intensely aware of himself as a significant living being.

Unfortunately it is true that in our culture there is much which interferes with the full realization of these potentialities for happiness. Some of this interference lies in the immediate environment of the child and in his constitutional endowment. Handicaps of a physical nature which might have passed relatively unnoticed in the previous age group now are emphasized as attention is more especially fixed on personal acceptability. Emphasis on success with the opposite sex in group activities makes the child increasingly body-conscious. Rapid growth and the often very abrupt appearance of features of sexual maturity predispose him to sensitivity about his appearance even when he is normally endowed. When he is in addition set apart by a marked difference, he finds social integration difficult indeed. Physical perfection is not a prerequisite for good adolescent adjustment; the most popular boys and girls are not necessarily those of outstandingly good physical endowment. However, marked deviations do complicate the problem.

The immediate environment is made difficult for the child of this age by parents who interfere with his attempts at emancipation, denying him the privileges of behaving according to the standards of his group as to dress, spending money, freedom in unchaperoned activities, lateness of evening hours, and the like. Other hardships in the environment may lie outside the parents' influence. A minority situation as to race, religion, or economic status has an adverse effect here as it does in the previous age periods, but without as much emphasis on the status of the family and more on that of the child himself. A boy or girl from an unaccepted family will, as he grows older, suffer fewer repercussions from community dislike of his parents. If he himself does not differ, if he conforms to group requirements as to appearance, behavior, and attitudes, his minority background may be ignored.

For the most part, the individual of this age is judged on the basis of his own worth as evaluated by his severe critics, his peers. If in any way their standards of behavior deviate from his, he will have to make rapid adjustments or find himself among the unaccepted. The marked intolerance of the adolescent peer group reflects, no doubt, the insecurity of its members. The young individual, feeling in himself strong compulsion to be independent and sophisticated, is quick to criticize any member whose inadequacy may build up his own sense of success. It illustrates the unfortunate human tendency at times of threat or insufficiency to point to others in an even more unfavorable situation. This hypercritical attitude intensifies competitiveness during adolescence and creates a demanding environment.

Defects in constitutional endowment and unusual severities of environment, however, account for a relatively small percentage of cases of maladjustment in this period. Of greater importance is the attitude which the adolescent has toward himself, toward his fellows, and specifically toward his own sexuality. These attitudes are the foundation stones laid in earlier years, which to a large degree determine success or failure in the transition to maturity. The boy or girl who enters adolescence burdened by concepts of his own inferiority, confused in his attempts at self-assertion, and guilty about his sexual feelings will not find in these years the happiness to which his heritage of youth should entitle him. When he was three years old he turned to the adults about him with questions about his origin and he used the responses they gave him in formulating his ideas of the way people live and love. If the curiosities and explorations of the young child were simply and frankly handled, the results are good when he is fourteen. If instead of a frank and honest response his queries evoked embarrassed or punitive reactions, he may unrealistically have repressed his interest or he may have rebelled in an excessive preoccupation with childish sexual activities, which established a depreciatory and promiscuous pattern for relationship between the sexes.

Intimidation or too violent rebellion expresses itself in character patterns of a poorly adaptive sort. These maladaptions are often either in the direction of withdrawal of all self-assertion or in the direction of exaggerated defiance of authority.

The withdrawn attitude shows itself in the boy or girl who takes little part in group activities, has few friends, and is generally the "wallflower." His retreat is evidence of the fact that he dare not express himself independently of parental guidance. As one aspect of the general repression he denies to himself his sexual feelings, concentrates rigidly on the "serious things" of life, such as reading and other solitary activities, and becomes involved in daydreams. If the pent-up sexual needs express themselves in masturbation, he feels guilty and his attitudes of inferiority are fortified. Not only are parents individually responsible for this unhappy state, but also the prevalent cultural traditions contribute to it. In spite of modern psychological teaching to the contrary, there is still much emphasis by youth leaders on the unacceptability of sexual feeling and particularly of masturbation, which is characterized as "self-abuse," the "hidden vice," and in like terms. To be sure, excessive masturbation as well as excessive sexual behavior of any kind is not to be encouraged, but to label it as sinful and shameful only makes it an activity carried on secretively and a source of much emotional conflict.

With so much that contributes to attitudes of guilt and confusion in the family and cultural milieu, it is not surprising that many withdrawn adolescents are unable to mature and remain emotionally dependent on their parents or other adults, sexually inhibited, confined by their own anxieties. They may or may not channel their energies effectively to achieve success in work, but in any case their capacities for free and happy lives are greatly impaired.

The other unfavorable type of adolescent adjustment goes in the direction of exaggerated defiance. This type of behavior is likely to emerge when the normal rebellion of this age is fortified by strongly hostile, antisocial feelings. The defiant child not only needs to emancipate himself from parental figures, he also feels the need to "get even" with them, and to highlight his rebellion by flagrantly antisocial acts or by sexual promiscuity. Such aggressive expressions are, of course, more likely to manifest themselves frankly in communities where delinquent groups exist and where the hostile boy or girl can thus achieve a kind of acceptance by his peers because of his antisocial tendencies. The same child in a better integrated community will in most cases express his resentments in less direct ways. In either case the deep hostilities are the motivation for much that is undesirable in character formation—undesirable both from the point of view of the individual and of society. Ruthless competitiveness, intolerance, poor sportsmanship, uncooperative individualism are some of the qualities which may become apparent as evidence of a poor foundation in interpersonal relationships.

The conflicts between love and hate which began in earliest childhood are poorly resolved if at this time the negative, destructive impulses overbalance the friendly, constructive ones. Then the adolescent's increased sense of independence and power acts to release in him an arrogant attitude toward his environment which, in one way or another, contributes to his own unhappiness and that of others.

The types of adolescent maladjustments represented by arrogant defiance of authority and by withdrawal occur in various degrees of severity and are not necessarily of serious prognostic significance. Mildly delinquent behavior as an expression of rebellion against authority often becomes increasingly less necessary as it is no longer so important for the young person to emphasize his independence. There is danger, however, that delinquent activities may create situations of practical difficulty, such as interference with school or work progress, unhappy marriage, or even involvement with the law. In addition, it is sometimes difficult for one who has been typed as an antisocial person to regain later the confidence of his group or to be able to accept without loss of face a socially responsible position. The pattern may tend for these reasons to persist and to affect the character of mature life, even though the need for it is no longer felt. In cases where hostilities are very deep, destructive attitudes become characteristic and affect the problems of adult adaptation, as we shall see later.

The withdrawn pattern similarly may give way to better group integration in the less self-conscious years that follow and leave only a memory of unhappy confusion, toward which the man or woman looks back with regret. When capacities for independence and self-expression are very deficient, however, withdrawal may establish itself as a permanent tendency. Then retreat and inhibition continue as handicaps to the attainment of maturity.

chapter 5

MATURITY: Adequacy and Overflow

> A man makes no noise over a good deed, but passes on to another as a vine to bear grapes again in season.
> —Marcus Aurelius: *Meditations*

It is easier to define the beginning of adolescence than its termination. Its onset is in general fairly well correlated with the objective signs of sexual maturity. The child's changed hormonal state and his awareness of physical alterations affect his concept of himself; they force him at this time rather abruptly to deal with new problems. We have observed that these problems are, first, the establishment of himself as an independent person, motivated by his own rather than by his parents' attitudes, and second, a satisfactory acceptance and integration of his greatly increased sexual feeling. Theoretically, once these problems are solved, the adolescent becomes a man or a woman. Such a point in any human life is obviously hard to recognize. In some lives it is never reached; in others there is vacillation between adult attitudes and regression into adolescent or childish ones which goes on throughout life.

At any rate, in our country the human being does reach the period of chronological maturity under the common law at the age of twenty-one. From approximately this time on it is assumed that he will no longer be so greatly preoccupied with the problems of emotional independence and sexual conflict; therefore he will be relatively free to function as an adult man or woman. He is now, we say, mature.

The terms used in a discussion of maturity and immaturity must be defined.

"Immaturity" is a label frequently applied to indicate the persistence of personality characteristics which belong in an earlier life period. Dependence on authoritative figures, tendency to shun responsibility, obvious self-centeredness, are commonly so labeled. Other traits may not be so readily recognized as belonging to a previous phase of development. For example, greedy possessiveness, compulsiveness, excessive rebellion, or undue conformity reflects the struggles which we have described as taking place in the pre-adult years. These and many other qualities could be listed as evidence of relatively unsatisfactory equilibrium in the mature role. Such a listing of negatives is of value in definition only if we can recognize in these qualities a common element.

In this case we may observe that the personality traits which we call immature are those which are concerned with *taking* rather than *giving*. The emphasis is still on achieving a buildup of self rather than on a more objective activity in the larger world. Again this distinction is, of course, relative. No one ever entirely loses interest in enhancing his own sense of worth; we only may say he lags in development if he remains so exclusively concerned with this need as to allow it to dominate the major interests of his life. In other words, it is assumed that the adult man or woman should be able to "take himself for granted" as an acceptable and independent human being and, with this assurance, function efficiently and realistically in his social milieu.*

Throughout the periods of childhood and adolescence, the young person is concerned with getting from the world that which he needs: first to sustain him physically, and second, to give him a sense of acceptance and power within his family group and in the social organization about him. In his search for this reassurance he relies at first strongly on parental figures as models and sources of strength; later he demands recognition on his own merits. This "taking in" motif determines much of the pattern of the child's early life. Curiosity and exploration enrich his apperceptive functioning; love that is given strengthens feelings of significance; skills learned are tools for manipulation and control. The child must be for the most part an absorbing creature.

Yet, from earliest years everyone has a capacity for giving, in returning love, in loyalties of friendship, and in acceptance of cooperative group activities. One's parents have been wise if they have contributed generously to his physical and emotional needs, while at the same time encouraging his consideration for the needs of others. In this way the foundation has been laid for the eventual attainment of an ability to give of one's self freely without experiencing a sense of self-depletion. This is the state of positive balance which favors efficient and constructive functioning in adult life.

This constructive, outgoing functioning of the mature person may perhaps be more specifically analysed, though it follows no hard-and-fast pattern. It is expressed in behavior which is responsible yet cooperative, independent yet ac-

* See T. Benedek, *Insight and Personality Adjustment* (New York: The Ronald Press Co., 1946).

knowledging realistic dependence, conforming to the needs of others while expressing originality and courage, trusting but not gullible. It is motivated by long-distance goals, but not compulsively so. Emotional balance is expressed in generosity of friendships and in ability to love steadfastly.

Because most of the hours of an adult's life are concerned with his work, the degree to which he has matured should, it might seem, be evident there. As an adult he should in his daily work not merely realize his need to sustain himself and to gain recognition, but beyond this he also should indicate his capacity to give—to manipulate the environment in such a way as to contribute something of social value.

This expression of mature attitudes in terms of a constructive work situation is, unfortunately, not always practicable. In our industrial and competitive culture, which demands that millions of men and women spend their working lives as mechanically moving parts of great machines, the work goal is obscure and unimportant to the worker. He must express his creativity (if he has it and if he has energies left over for expressing it) in other ways. Only the more fortunate minority who by reason of talent or circumstance have been free to choose their work according to their inclinations can be judged by their vocational performance, and here too the judgment is questionable. Shall we say the artist is mature because out of his intense narcissistic preoccupation he creates for the world a concept which illuminates a truth, enriches a feeling? What about the maturity of the successful salesman or advertising writer whose pleasure is in convincing his fellow-men of the (nonexistent?) value of a cough remedy? Are his efficiency and outgoing enthusiasm indexes of his adult status?

Using as a standard of maturity the capacity for giving freely beyond the needs of self-assurance, neither the creative artist nor the outgoing salesman is necessarily mature. The one, it is true, contributes a work of value, but his concern is his own experience; the contribution is secondary or is made for the sake of personal prestige. The other may enjoy his contact with people, but in his work he manipulates them merely for his own gain.

We could go on to apply our criterion to representatives of other vocations: the professions, politics, even religion and the research laboratories, and we should have to conclude bleakly that in our particular time and place one's success and even his social creativity reflect his intelligence, energy, and economic background more closely than they reflect his maturity. Such a correlation as does exist has more to do with the worker's motivation and his attitude toward his work than it does with his achievement per se. The mature worker seeks employment to be able adequately to support himself and his family; he does not shrink from the responsibility of assignments within his capacity; he is not handicapped by excessive dependence or by arrogant independence. It is not necessary that he use his work relationships or his accomplishments to bolster his uncertain self-esteem. It would appear, therefore, that a mature attitude provides the foundation for responsibility and consistency in one's vocational performance, but it does not assure outoutstanding success. On the contrary, the overcoming of such infantile qualities as greediness, strong competitiveness, and arrogant self-assertion tends to make the mature person less outstanding. His realistic drives to success are not as powerful as the more neurotic motivations which are often evident among leaders in their vocational groups. As to that, one can only comment that the world might be a better place with more mature people and fewer leaders in it.

If one's success in work is not a reliable index of his maturity, what about his play activities? We might observe, to begin with, that inasmuch as the child lives largely in a world of play and fantasy, excessive preoccupation with these activities is an indication of immaturity. Energies which could be constructively applied to work are expressed instead in search for diversion and pleasure. This criticism has to do with the quantity and exclusiveness of play and by no means denies its value. Play activities enrich life when they allow unharassed and unhurried hours for people to live together, to become aware of each other and enjoy interchange of thoughts and feelings, to join in games which are free of the serious and bitter competition of the world of work. It is good too to have some time alone for meditation, to share through books and music experiences which give additional beauty and meaning to life. Such play activities encourage the wider perspective which is characteristic of mature thought and feeling.

It is a pernicious phenomenon that in our day so much play activity lacks this quality of more intense living and instead consists largely of evasion of any deep thought or feeling. Not only is this situation indicative of the prevalence of immaturity, but the situation is conducive to its persistence. The most culpable of the escapist diversions are the passive, vicarious fantasies of television and the movies. The spending of hours upon hours of short and precious human life in a way which discourages interpersonal communication in favor of trite, uninspiring entertainment is a fact of our age not conducive to mature patterns of living. The unfortunate excuse for this impasse is the general lack of interest or motive in most work situations, plus the scarcity of intriguing hobbies in a highly technologic economy.

There is, however, more freedom possible in play than in work. The mature person need not follow the prevalent pattern. He is free to read, to walk in the forest preserves, or play ball with his neighbors. He may even have the opportunity to cultivate a garden and join in community projects. His initiative and persistence in escaping the prevalent vegetative use of leisure time are, it seems, some indication of his degree of maturity.

Maturity is, of course, revealed most clearly in the way people live together, particularly in close family relationships. Here the relative capacities for giving and taking are most evident. One must largely have overcome the absorbing, dependent quality of childhood if he is successfully to establish a family. He must first be capable of a heterosexual love relationship, which indicates a capacity for sharing as well as achievement of relative freedom from old sexual conflicts. Such a relationship does, of course, allow for much mutual support, providing in this way an acceptable gratification for the residues of dependency need which are present in every adult. The mutual quality of it preserves the equilibrium. One can to the highest degree enjoy giving to the person who gladly gives to him. If the relationship is one-sided it creates many conflicts. The dependent partner, not truly valuing his mate, provides no replenishment for that which he takes. Also, sensing his own needy and demanding state, he feels guilt which he may project as hostility. This is particularly evident in the dependent man who leans heavily on his wife but reacts toward her with irritation and defiance as though in that way to assert himself. Such a wife is in a difficult situation because a passive attitude on her part is frustrating to her husband, but if on the other hand she is obviously strong and supportive she becomes a threat to him. The emphasis in our culture on female dependence makes it easier for the woman to assume a taking role in marriage, contributing in this way to her husband's sense of power in a sometimes apparently satisfying situation. Such a marriage, however, lacks the inspiration of one of mutual helpfulness and often results in a sense of futility on the part of the wife and a search for reassurance in other relationships on the part of the husband.

The satisfactory achievement of a mature capacity to give is a solid foundation not only for a good marriage relationship but for successful parenthood. It implies a relationship with a child which is motivated by the welfare of the child rather than exclusively by the welfare of the parent. This reflects itself in all the aspects of child care: feeding and toilet training routines take cognizance of the child's physical and emotional needs; discipline becomes a logical part of the child's learning process, rather than an opportunity for a parent to dominate or to find outlet for his anger. The mature parent seeks to understand and guide but not to control his child. He values the child's achievements not for the sake of his own pride but because of the child's happiness in them. This ability to regard one's child as a separate individual, loved and guided but not smothered or coerced, constitutes the most fundamental quality of good parenthood. Immaturity in parents creates difficulties in children, which in turn retard the children's development, and thus the pattern is perpetuated.

The warm, outgoing qualities conducive to maturity in family relationships reveal themselves also in relationships outside the family. The adult person deals with his fellow-man realistically, with neither suspicion nor too great expectation. He is not threatened by the need to conform to social codes, does not feel that he must rebel for the sake of rebellion to preserve his own integrity. On the other hand, he is not so slavishly dependent on public opinion but that he dares to defy the code when this is indicated and to take a stand for the principles in which he believes. He is not afraid to compete, and enjoys active participation in a challenging situation at work or in play. However, the need to succeed is not so intense that competitiveness becomes a bitter and ruthless motivation.

Maturity is an ideal of responsibility and creativity which represents the full blossoming of human life. Its satisfactory achievement is determined by the years that have gone before and it in turn provides the basis for adjustments to be made to the problems of involution and senility.

chapter 6

INVOLUTION AND OLD AGE: The Problem of Self-Acceptance

> When we are young
> We long to tread a way none trod before,
> But find the excellent old way through love
> And through the care of children to the hour
> For bidding Fate and Time and Change Goodbye.
> —William Butler Yeats: *Land of Heart's Desire*

From a physiologic point of view, the period of involution (a retrograde change, the reverse of evolution) begins for the woman with the loss of child-bearing capacity. For the man it is less clearly defined, but similar hormone changes occur in him somewhat later than in the woman. There are evident at these periods structural alterations in the body which cause more or less physiologic discomfort. It is a state of biological disequilibrium, just as was adolescence, and it is followed after a few years by readjustment of the physical self in a somewhat modified way of functioning.

Psychologically speaking, however, the involution is not so closely correlated with bodily changes or symptoms as it is with changing attitudes. The renunciations and readaptations which supposedly parallel the physiologic process may occur quite independently of this process or may seem hardly to occur at all. Some people "retire early," using age as an excuse for narrowing activities long before this is physiologically indicated. Others continue in alert and creative activity well into advanced age.

Certain realities must be recognized by everyone who has passed his peak of vigor and expansive capacity. Physical buoyancy is diminished; he can no longer dash upstairs or dance unwearied through the night. The sexual challenge in personal relationships has for the most part receded. Adventure and exploration into the unknown continue to motivate only the fortunate few. Life's pattern has been pretty well established; opportunities for new experience are rare. The man or woman who continues at fifty or sixty to deny these realities and to hold desperately to the values he knew in former years fights a losing battle. He may cry with Thomas Wolfe, "Oh lost and by the wind grieved ghost, come back again," but it is a futile and pathetic cry.

In these middle years it is difficult to avoid frank self-evaluation. The glamorous fantasies of adolescence and the restless strivings of maturity can no longer successfully distract from the realization of one's actual situation. The central adaptive problem of the involutional period becomes, therefore, that of accepting one's self: of finding satisfaction in the way of life which one has established. Living with one's self is the hardest task of all, and this life period is one in which symptoms of maladjustment frequently occur. It is no longer possible to reassure one's self that the gains will be made in years to come. This is the time when one knows that dreams have been realized or renunciated; if they have been realized one must look at them and decide whether or not they were worth the effort they entailed.

Many situations interfere with the attainment of a harmonious middle age. One of these situations is ill health, which so often at this time restricts or curtails activity. It is obvious that some persons show the breakdown characteristic of the aging process much earlier than others. One's constitution undoubtedly influences his threshold of resistance against the bodily changes of old age. The relative importance of other factors, such as physical exertion, infection, nutrition, and the stresses related to social maladjustment is not clearly determined but it seems evident that all these factors play a part. Psychosomatic studies of such disabling illnesses as arthritis, hypertension, and diabetes suggest a relationship between the progress of the disorder and the patient's emotional state. Some of the more recent hormone studies emphasize the fact that excessive stress and strain, whether primarily physical or primarily psychic, arouse defense mechanisms in the body. These defensive reactions, when long continued, may create secondary changes in the tissues conducive to chronic illness. The specific location of the damage apparently depends on the individual constitution. Each person has his weak spots which are most susceptible to breakdown under strain. In other words, each person is endowed with a constitution which is more or less resistant to damage. This resistance depends largely on the tendency of certain organs to break down under stress. Whether or not chronic illness develops in later life depends then on the innate resistance plus the degree of traumatic (hurtful) experience. Experience may be hurtful in a directly physical way or it may act psychologically to arouse defensive reactions which disturb the bodily structure. Psychosomatic studies of these interrelationships have just been begun, and much remains to be learned. Whether or not the concepts will eventually throw some light on such scourges of later life as cancer and arteriosclerosis remains to be seen.

Whatever the causes of chronic illness may be, its existence is a limiting factor in adaptation. The limitation may be made use of by the person who wants an excuse to withdraw and allow himself the dependency he has never dared to accept before. He may, therefore, take advantage of, for example, a weakened heart or a rise in blood pressure and may fit himself into a relatively invalided life. In contrast, another person may find the physical disability excessively unacceptable, shutting off as it does his escape from himself into activity. He may insist on ignoring the damage even to the point of self-damage. The more realistic attitude is, of course, that of recognition of limitations without undue use of them.

One's resistance to the organic disabilities so prevalent in later age provides, then, an important determinant of good adaptation—a determinant which as we have seen is closely interrelated both by way of cause and of effect with the person's attitudes toward himself.

Another important determinant of one's capacity for self-acceptance as he grows old is the quality of his close love relationships. In the family husband and wife must depend now more than ever on each other. The children are grown and independent; the parents' mutual interests in rearing their boys and girls, which so often has been an important or even exclusive reason for their rapport, now no longer exists. At the same time absorption in work is diminished. The husband's schedule is less demanding, the wife's household tasks now relatively simple. There is time for leisure to be enjoyed together. Love which is deep and lasting is a beautiful thing in the later years. It has grown on experiences shared—joys which have been made more intense by the knowledge of the loved one's happiness, and sorrows which each has helped the other to bear. Such a love helps one to accept himself because he is accepted in the eyes of another person. If such a relationship has never developed, of if it has been broken by death, one must find support in children and friends—always an inadequate substitution.

Good health and a true love can help one bear a great deal of disappointment in his life. The person's actualities of success and failure are relatively less important than his constitutional buoyancy and the sense of emotional support upon which he can draw for sustaining himself. Success is, at any rate, a relative matter. To the competitive, driving person no achievement may ever seem sufficient and he tends to fret at the inactivity of his later years, to look with envy on all who have surpassed him. Obviously self-acceptance cannot be defined in terms of objective success.

We come back then to the basic attitudes which in every period of life have been observed to determine the quality of adaptation. The same infantile character traits which make it difficult to achieve maturity (which we have defined as ability to give without depletion) persist into involution to make self-acceptance difficult. And these traits in turn we know to be the product of unsatisfactory adaptations throughout the earlier years.

One attitude we observed to be a very important index of failure in the preceding life period: the attitude which demands constant reassurance of acceptance by others. It is obvious that this demand runs into increasing hazards as one grows older. The youth and young adult are at the peak of acceptability in physical attractiveness, strength, and mental alertness. With the years these qualities diminish—a universal phenomenon which some accept philosophically but to which others react with anxiety.

This is evident in the narcissistic woman who has found her greatest satisfaction in the admiration accorded her beauty. As its magic fails she tries, sometimes desperately, to preserve it. If she is blessed with a husband who sees her as forever beautiful she may be sustained in the illusion, but her chances of having such a husband are not too good in view of her own limited capacities as a wife. Other women have emphasized motherhood to the point of almost exclusive preoccupation with this role. Their pride is in the approval which they get from husbands and from the world in general. This is, to be sure, a motive of social value, but it is often associated with too great clinging to the children as they grow up and with a kind of smugness which demands gratitude of them. When they leave the mother's protective care she no longer has the sense of value which their need for her created.

A man's sense of acceptance by the world is usually related largely to his work achievement. If too much is staked on this the man dreads approaching retirement, resents the younger men's prestige, feels he is being "put on the shelf." Many such men decline rapidly after they quit working. They cannot accept themselves when they feel the world no longer admires and needs them.

A diminished capacity for sexuality is related to loss of beauty and child-bearing capacity in the woman and to loss of power in the man. If personal relationships have been highly sexualized, this diminution may be seriously threatening. The man to whom sexual potency has been an index of masculine adequacy is particularly affected. In women the valuable circumstance is often not so much the capacity for sexual feeling as the capacity to arouse this feeling in men. We have already observed that overestimation of this capacity predisposes to poor adaptation to aging.

One need not accept the poet's rationalizing, "The best is yet to be, the last of life for which the first was made." This is perhaps more in the nature of consolation than of fact, yet neither need one deprecate the potential values of the postmature years. Experience by this time has deepened the individual's understanding of himself and of others. In so far as he is no longer striving outward so competitively he has leisure for the desired but previously impractical preoccupations. Experience for its own sake, uninfluenced by economic or social gain, is easier to attain at this age. Friends who have remained true over many years take precedence over social contacts determined by business or prestige. Children now becoming established with their own families can still be a joy (without responsibility) to their parents. Much of the fresh outlook of earlier years can now be shared vicariously with them and with their children. Youth and its rewards are gone but the quieter, deeper, and less harassed experiences are rewarding in their own way.

Old age comes then to those who are—so we say—fortunate enough in heredity and avoidance of disaster to reach advanced years. Among the aged we can see clearly the importance of the attitudes which have been formed toward the world and toward the self. Even in the presence of severe disability the person who has lived harmoniously and constructively still preserves a sense of personal dignity and worth.

chapter 7

CHARACTER FORMATION

> How small of all that human hearts endure
> That part which laws or kings can cause or cure!
> Still to ourselves in every place consigned
> Our own felicity we make or find.
> —Samuel Johnson: *Lines Added to Goldsmith's Traveler*

WE HAVE attempted to define the basic problems of adaptation with which every person must deal in each life period, emphasizing the fact that failure in any one of these adaptations predisposes to superimposed failure, leading to vicious circles of maladjustment.

In the continuing interplay between the person as he is at any moment and the environmental demands of that moment there develops in everyone certain characteristic patterns of reaction. These typical reactions give him his individuality—constitute his character.

Formation of character is the product of three aspects of personality functioning which have been described by Sigmund Freud and labeled by him the id, the ego, and the superego. The id is the unsocialized aspect of the person, comprising his inborn drives for self-gratification without relationship to the rights of other persons and even regardless of physical realities of the external world. The young infant is motivated by these unsocialized drives; when he is hungry or uncomfortable he cries, when angry or frightened he screams. When his demands are fulfilled he is at ease.

Very soon, however, one learns to adapt his id-motivated behavior to the physical and social realities of the world about him, as we have already observed. This adaptation is accomplished by the integrating aspect of personality known as the ego. The ego is the adapting element per se, its activity being concerned with reconciling the diverse forces within the person and adjusting these forces to the environmental situation.

As adaptation becomes concerned more and more with interpersonal relationships it becomes influenced by codes of behavior of a moral quality and the person develops a relatively rigid set of standards of right and wrong behavior. This "moral sense" is the personality component known as the superego. It manifests itself early as the child takes over standards of behavior from the authoritative adults about him. He no longer regards these standards as imposed from without but now uses them as internal motivating forces. The character of any child's superego reflects, of course, the attitudes of his parents or parent-substitutes, and these in turn are influenced by the social mores of the group. One is aware of his superego as conscience—his conscious sense of right or wrong. A great deal of this moral aspect of personality functions unconsciously, however, as we shall see later.

It becomes clear, then, that the human ego must operate somehow among conflicting forces. It must make compromises not only with the external world but between the id and superego aspects of personality, reconciling the person's primitive drives with his standards of acceptable behavior. This represents the ego as a kind of buffer among inner and outer demands, a peacemaker and efficiency expert.

The ego, however, is more than a buffer. It functions in ways which early fall into the pattern unique for the individual: his character. We speak of "strength of character" on the basis of the qualities of ego functioning. Energy and flexibility of response, efficiency and variety of resources for adaptation, relative consideration for superego standards—these are some of the qualities of ego functioning which shape the individual character.

In general, the nature of anyone's permanent character traits is determined by the relationship which he establishes among id, ego, and superego components. His habitual tendency may be to follow impulse directly, motivated by his own desire for immediate satisfaction, or it may show a contrasting tendency to be strongly influenced by an exacting code to the point of inflexible behavior. Between these extremes is a relationship which efficiently compromises according to a realistic goal—constructive adaptation of the person within his social milieu.

The Dreamer

We observed in the discussion of adolescent adaptation that there are two character types which reflect an unwillingness to modify original impulse. One of these is expressed in the daydreamer, the other in the delinquent. The former avoids the harsh demands of reality by overlaying them with fantasy. He minimizes his dealings with the world as it is and in his daydreams compensates with one patterned to his heart's desire. This is a protective and consoling mechanism which to some degree is utilized by everyone. When, however, it becomes exaggerated to the point of substituting the dream for the necessary adaptation it leads to failure, hence necessitates the compensation of further fantasy which in turn favors further failure.

The daydreamer is the product of internal and external forces which make active adaptation difficult. Native energy (whatever that is) undoubtedly plays a part in determining one's degree of tolerance to frustration and demand. No child is a "born" daydreamer, but he is more or less predisposed in that direction according to his potentialities for vigorous self-expression. Interacting with native energy is the emerging concept of the self which is the product of experience. A child who lacks adequate encouragement, who is subjected to standards too difficult for his capacities, may retreat from his persistent sense of failure into his fantasies. We have observed that this retreat often becomes manifest during the stressful period of adolescence. The same retreat may be motivated also by parents who unrealistically stress family superiority. A "better than thou" concept inculcated by parents may handicap a child in his social acceptance and discourage group integration.

The history of the daydreamer is very often that of a person somehow made to feel set apart either by inferiority, superiority, or "difference" of some kind. He often harbors ambivalent feelings, according to which he is both an outstanding genius and a rejected incompetent. One girl, for example, reacted to a compliment by saying, "Of course it wasn't meant; I'm such an absolute nothing that no one could like me," but followed this by remarking later about the "stupid riffraff" she worked with, with whom she had "nothing in common." She described having, as a child, walked home from school along the less frequented paths so as not to be disturbed in her dreams, and she told of her terror when forced into group participation. She was encouraged by her parents to take singing and dancing lessons, on the basis of which she "fully expected to be a great movie star some day." On the other hand, the cold attitude of the mother, the father's drunkenness, and the general dilapidation of the home created a harsh reality. She said, "When I was twenty I suddenly began to get some impression of the world, and I was shocked and scared to realize what a little part of it I was, and how at that age I hardly knew anything about it at all."

The talented dreamer may express his fantasies in art forms which give him pleasure and which may incidentally win for him a kind of social acceptance. One such artist remarked, "I can't bear to sell or give away anything I have done—it's my self. If anyone should neglect or dislike a painting of mine I couldn't bear it." To this man, too, reality pushing in seemed overwhelming and unbearable. "Lying on the grass I opened my eyes and suddenly saw the huge world about me and knew that it was there and not a part of me, but something outside me, tremendous, incomprehensible. I shut my eyes again to keep it out and tried to build up the wall, not to see it, to live in my self."

The attempt to minimize the outer world, to return to the narcissism of early infancy, is an extreme manifestation of the daydreaming character. The lesser degrees of fantasy are more common, manifesting themselves in the person we see as shy, withdrawn, rather ineffectual, choosing the easier and less responsible roles in life.

The Antisocial Character

The delinquent character, like the daydreamer, rejects the demands for adaptation imposed by his environment. The delinquent pattern of maladjustment, however, is one that grows out of hostile interpersonal relationships. We have observed that a child's moral sense represents an internalization of the attitudes of his parents modified more or less by those of his peer group. The studies of sociologists * of city areas of high delinquency rate indicate that these are all seriously dilapidated sections in which the rate has been equally high whatever ethnic group of people live there. The deprivation and lack of social standards of such areas have an unfavorable effect on family relationships and favor an antisocial pattern of maladjustment.

Delinquent character in the broader sense is, however, not correlated with dilapidated areas. The wealthy delinquent has the advantage of being able to satisfy directly many of his impulses without lawbreaking. The irresponsible nature of his behavior shows most clearly in his lack of loyalty or stability in close interpersonal relationships. In the middle class, delinquent traits are conspicuous in the man or woman who resists application to any long-distance goal. Like the daydreamer, they want to realize their wishes immediately; but not being satisfied with the dream, they contrive in every way possible, by dependence or deceit, to gain easy satisfaction. Sometimes they are frank with themselves about their demands: "The world owes me a living." Others deny irresponsibility, finding excuses in the situation, claiming hard luck, blaming other persons. The degree of guilt varies greatly. In extreme examples of delinquency there seems to be little if any sense of wrongdoing. In other cases, guilt is strong and expresses itself at times in unconsciously self-punitive behavior. The person defies his superego but cannot "get by with it" and alternates between periods of irresponsible behavior and periods of depression,

* Clifford R. Shaw and H. D. McKay: *Juvenile Delinquency in Urban Areas* (Chicago: University of Chicago Press, 1942).

or gets himself, apparently by chance, into situations in which he is accused and punished. One such man said, "The cops took me in and beat me up plenty. I sat in jail and felt better than I had for a long time. The fear and tension were gone. When I got out I swore I wouldn't get into any more trouble." A few weeks later he was again involved in delinquent behavior.

Both the delinquent and the daydreaming characters are essentially immature. They lack that ability to give without depletion which has been discussed as characteristic of maturity. They hold back from active cooperation. They constitute no sharp categories of human behavior, however; everyone shows these tendencies to a greater or lesser degree.

I Am Persecuted

Another type of character, even more unfavorable socially, is not inclined toward direct expression of impulses but toward rationalization of failure. This is the paranoid character. This type of person is active, usually strongly competitive but suspicious and uncooperative. Success is tremendously necessary for him and he therefore tends to be intolerant of his failures. His mechanism of dealing with failure is denial of the fact by projecting the blame. This seems to have begun with Adam when he said, "The woman, she gave me of the tree," and with Eve who blamed the mute serpent!

Paranoid tendencies are widely prevalent in all competitive cultures. They are rampant in politics and business, and they create tremendous hazards for any minority group which becomes the focal point of blame. They intensify nationalism, making international dealings almost impossible. Because it is so difficult for human beings to live together harmoniously it seems necessary that they ally themselves by common attitudes against the "enemy."

These persecutory tendencies in a group may mean relatively little to the individual, being called out in him only by the dramatic appeals of the demagogues. He may, to be sure, lend himself to their pernicious doctrine yet have in himself no marked paranoid character traits. The mass of people who rally behind a paranoid policy do so for various reasons. Some of them may be influenced really to believe that the accused group is guilty. Some assume, "Where there is smoke there must be fire." Some join the group to avoid accusations of "appeasement" and some "to get on the band wagon." Probably only a few share this projection of blame because of their own paranoid character traits.

The paranoid character should, therefore, be considered apart from the expression of these tendencies in the cultural group. He is ordinarily a person inclined to be isolated from the group, self-centered, suspicious, unhappy. He is quick to feel rejected, defensive about the smallest failure. The typical life history is that of a person who has known little warmth and humor in his childhood, has been trained to place much emphasis on success. He approaches the world with a chip on his shoulder. If he achieves success he may have little need for paranoid ideas and will probably be considered a driving, dominant person. When and if he fails his basic suspicion and hostility will express themselves in attitudes of blame. "I didn't get a fair deal. It's all the fault of . . ."—this or that person or group. The ineffectual and greatly frustrated paranoid character may crystallize his persecutory ideas into a set of delusions and become psychotic. The dividing line between the sane and insane in this area depends pretty much on how many people agree that the accusatory idea is plausible!

We have seen that character structure takes form out of the struggles among diverse elements within the personality and the struggle for integration in an often hostile-appearing world. The types of reaction which we have just described express mechanisms for dealing with an external reality which for one reason or another presents difficulties.

Defense Against One's Self

There is another group of character patterns which give us insight into internal conflicts. These are the so-called overcompensatory traits. They represent exaggerated defenses against strong impulses toward behavior unacceptable to the person's own ego. A hostile desire to rebel, for example, may be concealed under rigid conformity, promiscuous sexual fantasies held in check by a Puritanical prudery, longings for dependent inactivity masked by perfectionistic or ritualistic work habits, arrogance denied by excessive meekness, or inadequacy defended against by arrogance. The fanatic, the moralist, the champion of the underdog, the martyr—all may be striving in these various ways by violent and active protestations to overcome the forces of evil or of weakness within themselves.

We do not assume, however, that all these attitudes and activities are merely neurotic compensations. They include much that is socially desirable. One person may be a moralist because his background of well-ordered and ethical family life has convinced him of the social value of a strong moral code. He will be more flexible and less self-righteous about it than the individual whose morality is used aggressively both against society and against his own impulses. The latter type of moralist is illustrated by the missionary in W.

Somerset Maugham's *Rain*, who kills himself rather than face the fact that he has offended against his own code.

One can distinguish the overcompensatory quality of a character trait by the rigidity and defensiveness with which it is held. If the compensation fails, the ego's control is threatened; hence the reaction is excessive. An arrogant attitude which expresses strong self-confidence can weather the storms of defeat but one which is a bravado against fear dare not acknowledge error lest the basic insecurity be revealed.

A distinction may be made between the process of overcompensation and that of sublimation. The latter is a useful mechanism of transfer of adaptive energies away from strivings toward unrealistic or unacceptable goals and toward aims which are socially approved. For example, a desire for domination, instead of being expressed in arrogant social attitudes, is gratified in executive or professional status; exhibitionistic wishes which originally had a sexual meaning lead into a career in politics or the theatre. In so far as the sublimation is of value in itself it makes for a satisfactory adaptation. If, however, these activities are but a cover-up for a persistent inner conflict, the character shows a rigid defensiveness typical of overcompensation.

Most altruistic social groups have some members motivated by a mature belief in the goals of the group and some motivated by unacknowledged needs of their own. To illustrate we may observe any group organized for the defense of an underprivileged minority. Many of the members are persons of the minority group or closely allied to it who have, therefore, realistic and laudable reasons to strive for its social betterment. In addition to these "native" members, there are those mature persons whose humanitarian interests go beyond self-concern. The third component is made up of the members whose participation has a neurotic meaning. They express in this way, relatively acceptable socially, some of their own repressed attitudes, such as their hostility for authority, their longing for power, their own sense of defeat and inadequacy. They may often be recognized by the ruthless and rigid way in which they "carry on for the cause."

People generally have the mistaken impression that the disorders known as neurosis and psychosis are clearly divided from normal behavior. The distinctions will be discussed in greater detail later, but it is important at this point to observe that the more serious disorders make use of the same adaptive processes which we are describing in relation to character formation. The withdrawn and paranoid mechanisms in more extreme degree are those of schizophrenia and paranoia, and the overcompensatory reactions are characteristic of neurosis.

We have observed character traits as typical patterns of ego adaptation to the demands of the outer world and to the conflicting forces within the personality. Obviously a character formation is successful in so far as it results in: first, a sense of harmony within the self, and second, a use of one's potentialities in ways that are socially and individually satisfactory.

Influence of the Biological Processes

In analyzing the factors which predispose to successful or unsuccessful patterning of character we may observe the effects of certain biological demands and the effects of demands superimposed by our cultural traditions. We have already considered the biological demands made by the various stages of maturation, emphasizing the importance of mastery of problems in their proper times. Applying these concepts more specifically to character structure, we see that a lack of success in one of the earlier phases of development tends to fixate character traits on the basic concerns of these developmental periods. The result is that relatively infantile preoccupations become the basis of permanent reaction patterns. It is as though one does not feel ready to cope with the increasing complexity of life and clings to his earlier satisfactions. In the earliest years these satisfactions were related largely to alleviation of the physical tensions of hunger and elimination. Around these functions are centered much of the young child's activity and the pattern of his character is affected by his preoccupation with them.

We apply the term, *oral character*, to the person who continues throughout life to have an "incorporative" attitude. He may continue to express this in his excessive concern with food as a means of gratification, overindulging in food and becoming obese or going on elaborate and ritualistic diets, or as a more acceptable sublimation becoming a gourmet or an accomplished chef. The essential orality may, however, transfer itself to other goals and be recognized in tendencies to "emotional greediness." The person of oral character takes rather than gives. He needs constant and excessive reassurance. His friends feel that he uses them, that he is parasitic, demanding, dependent. Progress toward maturity implies increasing capacity to give rather than take, hence the person of oral character has difficulty in attaining this state. Under the favorable circumstances of a life situation which gives generously to him he may, however, be able to give in return, but he reacts badly to deprivation, is excessively threatened by rejection.

The other strong concern of the young child which may color his character development is related to elimination. We have seen that toilet training represents for every human being the first issue of conformity or rebellion. In this regard the child is inculcated with two principles of correct behavior: cleanliness and regularity. His reaction to "training" is affected by his attitude toward those who impose the rules. If his relationship to the parent figure is good he will ordinarily accept the principles of adaptation which this situation involves without either too great protest or too great intimidation. If the relationship is not good the conflict may continue throughout life, expressing itself in various ways in his character pattern.

One may think of the issue of toilet training for the child as an expanding circle. In the center is the question of elimination per se, which demands neat and regular habits. Some persons remain fixed on this issue with resistance expressing itself in persistent constipation and much concern about bowel function, use of laxatives, and the like, or expressing itself in enuresis (bed-wetting) even into adult life. The conflict may be overcompensated in habits of great anxiety about defecation, need to eliminate every morning, and in general to follow a rigid routine in this respect.

Outside this central nucleus the issues of cleanliness so closely connected with it become attached. The person's character may be colored by his resistance to being clean. He dislikes bathing, prefers dirty clothes, often handicaps himself socially by his resentment of good grooming. We see this reaction often in the so-called Bohemian. Or here too there may be overcompensation in the form of excessive neatness and cleanliness, with meticulous attention to details. A bit of dust on the furniture or a lock of hair in disarray cannot be tolerated. This represents the overly trained person. Sometimes it is interesting to observe the rebellion showing through in, for example, the scrupulous housekeeper who neglects her own personal hygiene.

In its widest diameter the circle of activity originating in toilet training comprises even more abstract concepts having to do not specifically with elimination or even cleanliness, but with conformity and regularity in general. The issue expresses itself in stubbornness, retentiveness, and inflexibility.

Both oral and anal traits are commonly and easily recognized, and though they may predispose to psychopathology they are not ordinarily of such serious consequence. They are, however, handicapping characteristics, representing in a more or less nonspecific way preoccupation with early problems of sociobiologic adaptation.

Influence of Cultural Attitudes

In stating that character structure is affected both by biologic demands for maturation and by cultural demands we must recognize, of course, that these two sets of factors are constantly interacting. Biology demands that one eat and eliminate but society imposes its attitudes on these functions, as we have seen. This interplay is well illustrated also by the sexual function, which expresses itself directly in attitudes and behavior, but which has been subjected to very strong social mores. Its effect on the patterning of character is, therefore, determined largely by the person's concept of his own sexual acceptability according to the expectations of his group.

In our Western culture it is assumed that all males shall have "masculine" character traits defined especially in terms of aggressiveness and dominance, whereas all females shall be passive and receptive in character. The arbitrariness of this concept produces a good deal of conflict, because human beings do not always conform to its requirements. We have already referred to the sad plight of the little boy who becomes typed as a sissy or the little girl whose tomboy behavior persists into adolescence.

It is difficult to determine the relative importance of biologic versus social factors in developing masculine and feminine character. The boy, by virtue of his usually stronger muscular endowment and his more active sexual role, seems biologically predisposed to the more aggressive qualities. The girl, more delicately built and receptive in her sexual and childbearing functions, seems for these innate reasons predisposed to passivity. However, from earliest months of life the child is acted on by the expectation that he become a typical boy, she a typical girl. Brother is given toy guns and sister is given a doll; he is urged to be strong and active, she is encouraged in the less strenuous, more decorative behavior. The product as we see it is a culture actively determined in every field of endeavor by the men, which we must, therefore, evaluate as the result of interacting biologic and cultural phenomena. The situation is fair enough in so far as it is satisfactory to all concerned. Men get their satisfaction in work outside the home, which makes the home economically possible; women are happy in child rearing and maintenance of a well-ordered family life.

Unfortunately it isn't always this way. Deviations occur. Many men (for constitutional or early-environmental reasons) have strong longings for the more dependent, passive role of their wives and, vice versa, women often fret at the confining nature of their life situations, feeling the need for a position of more active social manipulation. In a relatively small group the deviation involves the sexual function itself and the person is, overtly or latently, homosexual.

This conflict between the cultural pattern of masculinity and femininity and the actual attitudes of the individual has several possibilities for expression in character traits. If the deviation involves homosexuality the person may live frankly according to his inclinations, associating with others of the same deviation, attaching himself to lovers of the same sex. The frankly homosexual man accepts a feminized style of dress, of mannerism, of vocational interest, and in his sexual life he responds to a man as a woman does. The same is true in reverse of the frankly homosexual woman. If the sexual deviation is not frankly accepted, it may be expressed in secret intimacies and in the choice of work and recreation which expresses the deviant interests in socially acceptable ways. Still more carefully concealed, even from conscious awareness of the person himself, latent homosexuality may be revealed in heterosexual maladjustment and vague dissatisfaction with the conventional life situation.

Conflict centering around the acceptance of one's masculinity or femininity does not necessarily involve the sexual function per se. The difficulty rather may be one of the individual's general interests and attitudes versus his idea of what he feels they should be. He may resolve the problem directly by following his own bent. In marriage the man may take the more dependent, the woman the more dominant role. He may take much interest in domestic matters; she may fill her time with vocational or avocational activities which allow her a stronger sense of control. If this is accomplished within community-acceptable limits and to the mutual satisfaction of the marriage partners the result may not be bad. There is, however, often some confusion in children whose parents to any noticeable degree depart from the conventional pattern.

A less well-recognized but actually commonly occurring manifestation of this problem in character is in the overcompensated masculine and feminine types. One example of this is the "Don Juan," who must by repeated conquests of women reassure himself of his masculine qualities. Similarly, the feminine coquette may be sexually frigid, expressing her power over men by exciting them but having little or no interest in actual sexual contact.

The individual may deny his sense of masculine or feminine inadequacy in other ways. The man might become a political dictator, expressing in a ruthless and grandiose way his denial of passivity. Not every dictator is overcompensating for a sense of masculine inadequacy, but some of their life histories suggest that this is by no means uncommon. With less energy and more limited opportunities, such a man may content himself by being dictator in his own home, playing the role so well that perhaps his family never suspects the doubts and fears which he covers in this way. The woman too may compulsively and meticulously follow the established womanly pattern, unwilling to acknowledge the resentment which expresses itself indirectly in many ways. The "martyr" mother's children may or may not recognize the hostility and domination under her acquiescent exterior. There are many possibilities for a "masculine" drive toward control to express itself in feminine ways.

If a deep sense of masculine or feminine inadequacy is not relieved by successful sublimation or overcompensation it may be manifested even more unfavorably in character formation. The person persistently unsure of himself in the social milieu is depressed and tends to withdraw, to establish a suspicious, "paranoid" attitude, or even to develop frankly neurotic or psychotic symptoms.

A less rigid cultural concept of masculinity or femininity, lending itself to better tolerance of the deviations which exist, would undoubtedly reduce social maladjustment. There do seem to be tendencies, in this country at least, in the direction of a more realistic modification of the concept.

Another cultural phenomenon predisposing to conflict is the marked incongruity between religious teaching and the competitive structure of our society. The Western world is for the most part dominated by the Christian religion. "Blessed are the meek" and "Love your enemies" represent the basic precepts of Christianity. Yet our social rewards go not to the meek, but to the arrogant. Much of the same incongruity exists within other religious groups.

This schism between the Church and the world outside tends to perpetuate religious ethics as a thing apart. The child reared in this situation develops a similar schism within himself. The moral teachings of the Church fortify those given by the parents. However, since in most instances neither his parents nor the Church members generally seem to follow these teachings, the child either does not take his religion seriously or, if he does, develops much guilt about his own inability to follow its codes of behavior. There is a tendency in this quandary to focus on the externals of religion, stressing belief in ritual and creed (one's own creed), often evading or disregarding the spirit of the teaching. The lack of consecration to vital and living religious ethics is deplorable. Much that is cynical and confused in character formation could be minimized by a sense of common belief in and striving toward the social goals defined by such a teaching. The experience of religion for the individual is to be sure not merely a code of ethics. This aspect is, however, most important from the standpoint of character formation, because of its influence on the superego or moral sense which determines to a large extent one's characteristic attitudes and behavior.

Toward Objectivity

It is good to be objective in evaluating character, whether this be one's own or that of the other person. To agree with Popeye the Sailor that "I yam what I yam" is to accept a static attitude that does not allow for any insight into the meaning of behavior. One does not have to like or even tolerate every character pattern, but one can deal with it more constructively by trying to understand what it represents. Why is one man "lazy," another "bossy," one woman "self-sacrificing," and another "a gossip"? What is the meaning of my own sensitivities and anxieties?

We may allow all due credit to inherited constitution as a factor determining anyone's ease of adaptation, yet the manner of his adaptation (his character) is not a simple, inherent unfolding like the automatic workings of an insect. Its emergence is a dynamic process involving brain cells, cultural codes, mother's love, wise words, digestive processes, clouds against the sky. All these components of life and thousands more working in and on human protoplasm shape a person who has a name and a brief place on our whirling planet. By what we see of his behavior and by what he can tell us of himself we judge his character.

PART II

Adaptations That Fail

chapter 8

ADAPTATIONS UNREALISTIC AND INEFFICIENT: Neurosis

> And how am I to face the odds
> Of man's bedevilment, and God's?
> I a stranger and afraid
> In a world I never made.
> —A. E. Housman: *Last Poems*

W<small>E HAVE</small> observed that in the continuing interplay between the individual and his environment there develop certain reaction patterns which are typical for the individual, which represent his habitual ways of responding: his character. It is obvious that character types are not always well suited either for securing the happiness of the person concerned or for making him a useful and acceptable group member. They represent reactions often strongly defensive or overcompensatory. They often carry over into adult life responses that may have been suitable in an earlier age but that continue to be applied too rigidly and indiscriminately. The tendency to retreat, for example, holds one back even in situations where success might easily have been achieved, and a strong perfectionism limits unnecessarily the scope of activity.

The line of division between such handicapping character patterns and the handicapping symptoms which are labeled neurosis is by no means clearly drawn. We see this as we attempt to define neurosis.

What Is Neurosis?

Let us say that neurosis is a disorder of function representing unrealistic and inefficient attempts at adaptation under difficult circumstances. The attempts are unrealistic and inefficient because they do not deal frankly with present reality as it is but represent fixed reactions related to internal conflicts and regressive evasions of reality. There is in neurotic symptoms a kind of repetitive compulsiveness. It is as though in these symptoms the person attempts over and over to resolve internal and external conflict, but blindly, unable or afraid to face the real issues.

To clarify the situation, we might observe that neurotic reactions manifest themselves in three large and overlapping ways: as neurotic character, as somatic neurosis (bodily illness), and as symbolic symptoms (the neuroses per se).

Neurosis in Character

The neurotic element in character is probably never entirely lacking in anyone. We have assumed that a character pattern is satisfactory (that is, nonneurotic) in so far as it accomplishes internal harmony ("peace of mind"), and at the same time favors the individual's use of his potentialities in socially valuable ways. Anyone, then, is more or less neurotic, judged by his own subjective state and his usefulness and acceptability in his social group. Character traits such as excessive suspiciousness or a strong sense of inadequacy may not be as obviously pathologic as phobia, but they are likewise a handicap, and likewise represent repetitive reactions applied unrealistically. These neurotic elements in character structure have been elaborated on in the previous chapter.

We might emphasize again that the static concept of the self held by most persons is unfavorable to progress. If one assumes a "That's the way I am" attitude toward himself he fails to recognize that his typical behavior is a cause-and-effect phenomenon not necessarily desirable and not unmodifiable.

Individuals vary a great deal in their capacity for self-evaluation or insight. Some seem quite completely incapable of it. To be sure, it is always much easier to see the other person's lacks in this respect than it is to see one's own. Traits easily recognized by others as malicious "snoopiness" are rationalized by their possessor as interest in other persons. Rudeness is accepted in one's self as frankness, aggressive dominance as strength, hostile rejection of others as "reserve." Socrates was indeed expressing a fundamental truth when he said, "Know thyself." It is a question, however, whether or not Socrates applied this principle very efficiently in evaluating his own personal life. Undoubtedly a great deal of the difficulty which people have in living together harmoniously is due to human inability or unwillingness to view objectively the neurotic elements in their own characters. Perhaps in a less insecure world this would be more readily possible, but in a less insecure world there would be less need for neurotic defenses. It is a vicious circle. Maladjusted persons make a maladjusted society which in turn favors further individual maladjustment.

Neurosis in Bodily Illness

Neurotic tendencies which reveal themselves in bodily symptoms express poor adaptation in physiologic rather than in sociologic ways. The background may be similar. An overly anxious attitude may be the basis for chronic digestive disorder or it may underlie the formation of tense, compulsive character traits. A deep, long-continued sense of resentment may produce a delinquent character or a state of elevated blood pressure.

Why does dissatisfaction in one person disorganize the bodily state and in another person express itself in his habitual attitudes toward his fellow-man? The answer to this question involves an evaluation of many contributing factors. There is the poorly understood element of organ resistance. There appears to be much constitutional variation in vulnerability to physical illness. Some from early years are prone to digestive disorders, others to skin conditions, headaches, endocrine disturbances. Some persons seem more susceptible than others to infectious processes. On the other hand, the social environment often favors illness. An anxious parent may assume that a child is "frail"; a tradition thereby established persists as a chronic tendency to preoccupation with illness. A person whose rigid training in repression does not allow him to express his hostility in character traits may have severe headaches as substitutes for temper tantrums.

There has been a good deal of interest lately in what is known as psychosomatic illness. This interest reflects a growing awareness of the fact that many of the symptoms which bring the patient to a physician cannot satisfactorily be understood in purely organic terms; in fact no significant organic pathology can be found. To the physician the fact that approximately half his patients fall into this category is frustrating, inasmuch as his training has equipped him to treat skillfully the sick body but has given him not much preparation for dealing with personal maladjustment. In this dilemma he has tended to react in one of two ways. He may assure the patient that nothing is wrong with him and urge him to "snap out of it." His patient will usually go to another doctor, hoping to find elsewhere some acknowledgment of distress, or he may, as many do, attempt to find relief in a cult of some kind. Other physicians may feel that in the presence of symptoms there *must* be organic pathology of some sort and may try to "build the patient up" by directions as to diet, medications, and rest. Such an attitude may help by gratifying dependency needs; it may on the other hand establish even more firmly the tendency to invalidism.

Any attempt to treat body and mind as separate entities is based on an unrealistic assumption. The living organism is not composed of separate parallel functions but is a unit, active in ways that may be primarily physical or primarily psychic but always with some degree of total involvement. Digestion, for example, usually seems to have little psychologic significance, yet one's outlook is definitely affected by his state of nutrition and by the satisfactory nature of the processes involved. Not only does digestion affect the mood, but also the mood affects digestion. Everyone is familiar with dry mouth, nausea, or diarrhea as response to emotional upset. Any state of strong feeling is experienced not merely in abstract gladness, fear, or anger, but in physical symptoms of muscular tension, trembling, choking, laughing, weeping, and in numerous bodily changes of which one is not aware.*

The tendency of physicians not to deal frankly with the emotional aspect of illness reflects a widely prevalent attitude of evasiveness toward anything which might be considered a personality disorder. The doctor hesitates to suggest to the patient that his "heart" symptoms are evidence of a tense, overanxious attitude based on disturbing elements in the patient's life. He hesitates because he himself does not know how to treat such a condition and also because he knows that his patient might be humiliated or angered by the diagnosis. The idea in general is that one is not "responsible" for an organically damaged heart but that an emotionally disturbed heart is indicative of character weakness or instability.

This concept is one which retards progress in therapy. It is much better to concede that most human beings are socially more or less maladjusted, and that in a certain rather high percentage of them this maladjustment expresses itself in disorders of bodily function. Obviously the rational treatment for such disorders is directed toward the causes of the maladjustment rather than toward the heart, stomach, or other organ involved in the reaction.

The Meaning of Anxiety

The simplest bodily manifestation of emotional disturbance is in the physical symptoms characteristic of anxiety. They are universal, not only among mankind but among the

---

* F. Alexander and T. M. French, *Studies in Psychosomatic Medicine* (New York: The Ronald Press, 1948); F. Dunbar, *Mind and Body* (New York: Random House, Inc., 1947); R. R. Grinker, *Psychosomatic Research* (New York: W. W. Norton & Co., Inc., 1953).

lower animals. Dr. Cannon * has designated them as a preparation for fight or flight. The heart rate is increased, muscles are tensed, digestion is at a standstill, blood pressure is elevated, pupils are dilated. It is a mass reaction to danger. In most human instances, however, the response cannot be expressed either in fight or flight; hence, instead of serving as a preparation for better adaptation, the anxious reaction in fact disorganizes the bodily processes. Attacks of accelerated heartbeat, difficulties in breathing, digestive disorders, trembling or dizziness, weakness, are often the manifestation of the nonspecific disorganization resulting from anxiety.

We think of anxiety as differing from fear in its less clear relationship to external danger. Fear is a response to a specific threat; anxiety is a more diffuse reaction to a poorly defined or consciously unrecognized danger. The chronically anxious person is often quite unaware of the meaning of his apprehensiveness and tends to fix it on one thing or another indiscriminately.

Studies of anxiety reactions indicate that the disturbance is essentially related to a threatened loss of ego control. We have defined the ego as the integrating aspect of the personality, which has two functions. The one function is the preservation of harmony within the self, attained by reconciling the demands of the id and the moral standards of the superego. The other ego function is concerned with adaptation to the realities of the outer world. The ego adjusts one's behavior to the necessities of external reality and at the same time compromises between one's primitive desires and one's moral standards of behavior.

The balance achieved by the ego is a more or less unstable state, which may be disturbed by intensified external de-

* W. B. Cannon, *The Wisdom of the Body* (New York: W. W. Norton & Co., Inc., 1932).

mands, particularly by a situation which tends to fortify either id or superego components. For example, many men who were able to lead well-organized lives as civilians broke down in military service, with symptoms of intense anxiety manifested both in bodily symptoms and in their subjective states. Their previously efficient balance was upset by such factors as id aggressiveness resulting from arbitrarily imposed authority and superego guilt related to this aggression. In such a situation conflicts develop between a wish for self-preservation and an inculcated drive to be brave. The physical-emotional symptoms which develop are essentially the manifestations of fear of loss of ego control.

Anxiety That Overwhelms

The frankest expression of this kind of disturbance is in the very commonly occurring syndrome or group of signs and symptoms, known as *anxiety state*. The symptoms are those universally expressing fear, manifesting themselves on both a physiologic and a psychic level. They may be experienced acutely as "anxiety panics." These distressing symptoms appear suddenly, often without known cause. The bodily symptoms may be predominant, taking the form of rapid heartbeat, difficulty in breathing, nausea or diarrhea, sweating, trembling, or feelings of weakness. In other cases these symptoms may be relatively insignificant and the patient may complain rather of a state of acute apprehensiveness in which he feels about to die or to "go crazy." The more chronic anxiety states are manifested in persistent weakness and tension. Here too the emphasis may be on physical illness so that the person becomes hypochondriacal, or it may rather take the form of a chronic undercurrent of anxiety and apprehension which attaches itself to one situation or another or remains "free floating."

Anxiety state represents disequilibrium per se. Like all disequilibrate conditions in nature, it tends to resolve itself. The resolution, however, does not always go in the direction of a reasonable and satisfactory settlement of the conflicts involved; it may follow a neurotic pattern, as we shall see later.

Anxiety must be reckoned with not only as a cause of illness but as a complication of organic illness. The person who worries excessively, whether realistically or not, about his pathological condition, may confuse his physician by adding symptoms which express his emotional turmoil. Also, his attitude toward his life situation in general may affect the efficiency of his recovery. Apathy or despair is not conducive to good convalescence, as every observant physician knows.

In conditions such as cardiac disease, high blood pressure, diabetes, epilepsy, disfiguring skin conditions—to list only a few—the patient's attitude is of much significance. Much unnecessary invalidism results from fear or humiliation or from an uncooperative rebelliousness. The sick child needs particularly careful handling to prevent the development of chronically depressed or fearful concepts and to insure a willing participation in a therapeutic regime.

Neurotic Disturbance and Organic Change

Anyone can rather easily recognize the role of emotional disturbance in creating symptoms of acute anxiety and in complicating the processes of organic illness. It is somewhat more difficult to assess the relative roles of the physical and psychic levels of activity in the causation of structural change. One cannot simply say that the illness is organic if structural damage can be demonstrated, and neurotic if there is no such damage. Many conditions which are obviously precipitated by psychologic stress and strain (as, for example, spastic colitis) may bring about in time some changes in the organ involved. A long-continued unwillingness to eat, expressing a neurotic state, will cause such secondary bodily changes as cessation of menstruation, lowered blood pressure, extreme muscular weakness. This is dramatically revealed in the extreme attitude of revulsion toward food known as *anorexia nervosa*.

Many diseases which in previous years were considered only in terms of organ pathology now are viewed as so-called psychosomatic disturbances. They include not only conditions which can obviously be seen to be related to emotional disturbance, such as high blood pressure and migraine, but also many in which the relationship is more obscure, such as arthritis and stomach ulcer. Even a fractured bone, which outwardly appears as a clearly physical phenomenon, may be basically the expression of a neurotic accident-proneness.

This is not, of course, an all-or-none situation. The presence of psychologic conflict of a more or less specific sort has been demonstrated in many of these illnesses but this does not rule out the element of organic predisposition or, in some cases, of acquired organic damage, which makes the patient more susceptible to this particular kind of disorganization. Neither does it rule out the need for medical treatment once damage has occurred. This need for a "total" approach might be illustrated in relationship to the patient with an ulcer of the stomach. The typical history of such a person is that of one who is outwardly active and ambitious but who on closer examination reveals strong longings for a more dependent, passive, receptive role. These repressed "oral" traits are believed to be related to the tendency of his stomach to secrete an excessive amount of gastric juice, which over a period of time irritates the stomach lining and causes the ulcer. Such patients are advised to cultivate a more relaxed, less driving pattern of living to accept more frankly their needs for passivity. At the same time they are treated symptomatically by diet and medications to allow the broken-down tissues to undergo repair. There must be recognition, too, of the fact that the stomach in this particular person is *vulnerable* to emotional disturbance. Another person with a similar conflict might express it in other ways.

Some illnesses with psychologic elements have a clearly constitutional background. The allergies, for example, represent inherited tendencies to overreact to stimuli in specific physiologic ways. The stimuli may be either physical or psychic or a combination of the two. A man with asthma was observed to have an attack whenever exposed to cold, damp weather. He also had a series of attacks in good weather when he was involved in emancipating himself from his mother. Sensitivity to the same foods varies in some allergic individuals and the variability seems to be related to their emotional state at the time. The clinical record of a woman with severe eczema and asthma indicates that she was brought in frequently for treatment during her extremely deprived, unhappy childhood. In early adolescence she made a good adjustment in a foster home and the visits diminished. She then married a man who proved to be not only abusive to her but also a bigamist. At this time the condition flared up severely again. After her divorce and during a subsequent happy marriage symptoms diminished. However, several years later she gave birth to a son and when in infancy he showed symptoms of the mother's disorder she came back to the clinic with extreme exacerbation of her own symptoms.

Patients of this type can be satisfactorily treated only "as a whole" with recognition of the fact that satisfactory human functioning even on an organic level is determined at any time by the ability to adapt to the life situation at the time. An organ relatively weak in a situation that is either physically or psychologically disturbing results in symptoms indicative of disorganization. If this disorganization is clearly a functional response of the organ to psychologic disturbance we call it a somatic (body) neurosis. If the cause involves an interrelationship of physical and personal elements we call it a psychosomatic illness. Obviously the grouping is arbitrary and it is to be hoped that in time such distinctions will no longer be made, as patients and physicians alike recognize the need to weigh carefully all the disturbing circumstances in every case of illness.

In the conditions we have been describing we see a neurotic kind of adaptation expressing itself either in character traits or in a tendency to physical illness. We call these adaptations neurotic because they represent repetitive reactions which are not well suited for solving the situational problem. Ordinarily their real meaning is not apparent to the individual involved. He tends to regard his character as the way he was born and his illnesses as the result of organic damage or inherent weakness. They become in this way firmly fixed and may persist throughout his lifetime unrecognized and untreated.

Neurotic tendencies expressed in character traits or bodily illness are of such frequent occurrence as to be accepted within the normal pattern of life. When, however, these tendencies express themselves symbolically—in neurosis per se—they create relatively bizarre symptoms and it is then generally recognized that the person suffers from a psychologic disorder.

Symbolization in Neurosis

The tendency to symbolize conflict in neurotic symptoms indicates an unwillingness or inability to deal frankly with a difficult life situation. These symptoms fall into specific categories and have a similar meaning and purpose for all patients. They include the phobias, the conversions, the obsessive-compulsive states, some depressive conditions, and the various types of behavior expressing irrational impulsiveness.

A study of these "classical" neuroses is of tremendous interest in relation to the meaning and the mechanics of human behavior. To understand them we must recognize powerful forces operative within every person outside the limited scope of his consciousness. These unconscious forces affect one's actions and mood, often determine the goals which he sets up for himself, yet are not accessible to conscious thought processes.

The Unconscious

Most persons are more or less vaguely aware of the existence of an unconscious (sometimes called subconscious) element in their functioning. They are amazed when they suddenly remember events long absent from thought and presumably forgotten. At times they may realize that certain tendencies to forget indicate a wish to forget which has operated unconsciously. "Slips of the tongue" too are often admitted as unconsciously motivated expressions of an unacknowledged thought or feeling.

"Unconscious" and "forgotten" are not synonymous. That which is forgotten may no longer be operative, may leave, so far as we can tell, no trace. Telephone numbers we knew ten years ago, the lists of battles and dates learned in history class, dinner menus of last year, these and thousands of other unimportant facts do not continue as a part of one's mental equipment.

Neither is "unconscious" synonymous with "preconscious." The preconscious experience may at any time become conscious; it meets no resistance. One may, for example, be carrying on a conservation in a room where music is being played or where the temperature is uncomfortably cold. Absorbed in the conversation, one is unaware of the music or the chilliness, but at any time his attention may focus on one or the other and the preconscious becomes conscious.

The unconscious, then, differs from the forgotten by being still operative and from the preconscious by being, under most circumstances, not voluntarily accessible. It is the great reservoir of thoughts, feelings, and potentialities which have been repressed—that is, denied conscious recognition.

The Process of Repression

This "keeping unconscious" process of repression is manifested early in life as the child avoids serious conflict by denying the conflictual drives within himself. We have seen that the gradual process of maturation involves giving up old patterns and establishing new ones—constantly adapting to a changing biologic state and to new environmental demands—and we have recognized the internal conflicts inherent in this process. The ego finds difficulty in reconciling such situations as hatred of a parent versus strong codes of loyalty, dependent longings versus pride in achievements, sexual desire versus prudish and anxious attitudes about sexuality. The process of repression represents a way of avoiding impasse by keeping one's self unaware of certain segments of experience which are unacceptable to the ego. These experiences, heavily charged with feeling, remain unconscious, we say, though they have not been eliminated and may in various ways affect behavior. For example, the child may repress his longings for dependence, covering them with a façade of active, aggressive behavior, and he is not aware of the existence of these longings. His idea of himself as he matures is that of a strong and independent person. The dependency manifests itself in indirect ways, some of which we have already described: proneness to accident or illness, overcompensation in irritability and pugnaciousness in responsible situations, flight into alcoholic episodes, and many other such ways suggestive of disequilibrium.

Repression is not a deliberate, voluntary process, but operates automatically. It differs in this way from suppression, which is a more casual, voluntary process. For example, one is expected to go to work when his inclination is to stay in bed. He suppresses the latter wish though with some conscious regret. The distinction between repression and suppression is, however, not entirely clear-cut, as attitudes repeatedly suppressed come in time to be kept unconscious without deliberate effort. This occurs in the process of maturation as the child comes more and more to behave in socially accepted ways which have become habitual to him.

The purpose of repression is an economic one in that it automatically regulates behavior in the direction of a social goal without necessitating a constantly operating process of voluntary self-discipline. Its disadvantage lies in the fact that, since it operates unconsciously, the conflicts with which it deals are not amenable in later life to rational decisions. Many of the most important repressions are established in early life and concern problems with which the child is incapable of dealing in a frank, direct way. These same problems may be by no means so insoluble to the adult, but being repressed they are not accessible to him. There is, for example, the ambivalence of the young child in relation to his parents. A girl dominated, overprotected, and intimidated by her mother may grow up repressing the deep hostility with which she is unable to deal and may, as an adult spinster living with this mother, deny any but the most righteous feelings about her. The repressed hostility expresses itself in other ways, and actually might be better dealt with consciously as a logical reaction to severely thwarting circumstances. Another example is the repression of sexual interest which is so often forced on the intimidated child. In his helpless dependency he dare not face his sexual interests; in later life he could do so, but the pattern of repression is by then firmly established. He only knows that he is incapable of sexual feeling or that it expresses itself in deviant ways.

Individuals differ as to the burden of repression which they carry into adult life. The more fortunate ones are those who have been encouraged in a relatively frank and fearless handling of the emotionally charged situations with which every human being must deal. Attitudes unacceptable to society and to the person's own superego have in these cases been not blindly repressed but recognized and renunciated. The energies of these strivings can then be utilized in other fields of activity—in the well-known process of sublimation. Repression is, as has been mentioned, a valuable tool of adaptation, but when it is excessive it predisposes to instability.

Preservation of Equilibrium

We see, then, that personality equilibrium is determined by a balance between the repressed and the repressing elements. This amounts to a continuing conflict in every person between those primitive tendencies of the id which must be kept inactive and, on the other hand, the repressing forces of ego and superego.

In our discussion of anxiety states we pointed out that this condition represents neurotic disequilibrium per se. The patient's experiences (physiologic or psychologic) have acted to reinforce repressed elements or to weaken the repressing elements. His anxiety, therefore, expresses his sense of confusion and his fear of loss of ego control. Such an unstable state is very distressing, inasmuch as nothing is solved by it and the patient gains nothing from it.

Other neurotic states avoid this intense discomfort by unrealistic and inefficient mechanisms of adaptation. Their symptoms represent displaced and symbolized expressions of the repressed strivings, or intensified protection against these strivings. In some cases they represent a compromise between denial and gratification.

Anxiety Hysteria

Anxiety hysteria, or phobic state, illustrates these mechanisms in a fairly simple way. The patient with a knife phobia, for example, is often more or less aware that his fear of knives represents fear that he will harm someone. He is seldom aware, however, of the meaning of the hostility which he guards against in this symbolic way.

A phobia may focus on any object or situation, but some are so common as to be considered classical and have been given Greek names. The frequent occurrence of these particular phobias probably indicates their suitability for representing common human conflicts. Agoraphobia, the fear of open spaces; claustrophobia, the fear of closed spaces; erythrobia, fear of blushing, are some of these. Other common symptoms are fear of high places, which is related to a fear of jumping and is often associated with a fear of throwing one's self in front of moving vehicles. Phobias for spiders, bugs, and reptiles are so common, especially among women, as to be considered often as the product of cultural conditioning. Even the pleasantest of experiences may become phobic—as in, for example, a music phobia or a traveling phobia.

Some phobic tendencies are no doubt present in most people, but they are ordinarily relatively insignificant and under control. In their developed form in the anxiety hysteria patient they assume much importance and seriously handicap functioning. This patient's activities are to a large extent determined by his attempts to avoid that which he fears. If by circumstance he is forced into the phobic situation he experiences great fear and shows the outward manifestations of a terrifying experience.

An unfortunate feature of the phobic state is its tendency to spread out, involving more and more situations, thus progressively hampering the patient. One who begins for example, with a fear of knives may go on to develop fear of all sharp objects or of all steel objects, of kitchens and workshops and even of stores where such objects are kept. The phobia then may develop secondary objects, such as the dress worn in the kitchen or the hands of a person who recently handled a knife. Such a spreading-out process indicates the inefficiency of the symptom as a protection against the repressed, so that the defense must be continually widened.

The essential process involved in the development of a phobic state is an attempt to represent an internal conflict in an external situation and then to avoid that situation. The anxiety, instead of being frankly and diffusely experienced as it is in anxiety state, here is circumscribed. In so far as one can avoid these externalized symbols of the conflict, one can be at peace. It illustrates, however, as we have observed, the inefficient nature of neurotic adaptation. The person, not aware of the true nature of his conflict (because it is repressed), acts blindly and frantically, and his failure to establish a real sense of resolution of his problems leads him often into progressive self-limitation.

The simplest phobias are those which are directly a reinforcement of repression, in which one avoids something which represents his unacceptable impulses. In other cases the process is less frank and expresses in addition fear of punishment for the unacceptable impulses, or allows some gratification of these impulses through preoccupation with them.

For the most part the element of neurotic gain is minimal in anxiety hysteria. Such symbolic forms of gratification as may exist are certainly by far overbalanced by the restrictions imposed and the sufferings experienced in the phobic situation. Since this so-called secondary gain in any neurosis tends to perpetuate the disorder, we should expect prognosis to be relatively good in phobic states, and this on the whole is true. Those patients who can be made aware of the meaning of their phobias and are cooperative in attempting to analyze and overcome them have a high rate of recovery. The phobia is more persistent if it is associated with generally poorly adaptive character traits. Here the symptom is only the most obvious manifestation of the patient's maladjusted state and cannot satisfactorily be eliminated without profound changes in basic attitudes. When, for example, the patient's ego is incapable of recognizing and analyzing his deeply hostile attitudes toward others, when he dare not question his concept of himself as a righteous and mature person, then it is difficult to eliminate the symptom which expresses his guilt and fear. Neurotic defenses of all kinds are built up out of weakness and once formed they are conducive to increased weakness. In this vulnerable state one is reluctant to give up the defenses he has, even if they are manifestly inefficient and unrealistic.

Conversion Hysteria

Another neurosis which symbolizes and circumscribes conflict, but by way of physical symptoms, is *conversion hysteria*. Here a certain body function becomes disturbed in a manner which serves again either to defend against repressed impulses or to compromise with them.

The symptoms of conversion hysteria involve for the most part those bodily functions which serve in contacting the external world: the muscles, the skin, sensation in general, and the special senses. (This is in contrast to the symptoms of anxiety state and somatic neurosis in which the organs of internal integration are involved: digestion, heart action, breathing, sweating, and the like.) Common conversion symptoms, therefore, are paralyses, loss of sensation in a part of the body, or blindness, deafness, mutism, convulsive states. Less common are the hysterical fugues during which one behaves in an automatic way dissociated from his life pattern and retains later no conscious memory of the episode. These are the so-called amnesic states.

Conversion hysteria is a neurosis with a long and interesting history. It was apparently more common in the past than it is now and its bizarre symptoms led to much conjecture and to interpretations that ranged from demoniacal possession to special favoritism of the gods. The name *hysteria* (*hystera*—"womb") was applied by Hippocrates who rightly sensed the sexual nature of the illness and, believing that it occurred only in women, named it thus to indicate that it represented the activities of the frustrated and wandering "womb."

It might be remarked at this spot that the word "hysteria" is one which is used in so many poorly defined ways that it might be better if it were discarded entirely. Anxiety hysteria is more adequately described as phobic state, and conversion hysteria as conversion state. "Hysterical behavior" as loosely applied covers a multitude of disturbances that may have little in common, and certainly are not adequately described in terms of a "frustrated womb"—particularly as they are to be found in men as well as in women.

However, there was much of wise intuition in Hippocrates' interpretation of conversion hysteria. In the later "dark" eras of history this concept of a disorder related to emotional conflict gave way to the ideas of supernatural possession. Many conversion patients undoubtedly were put to death as witches; others succeeded in using their symptoms to suggest divine power. The responsiveness of conversion symptoms to various forms of suggestion has always given this neurosis a sensational quality. The phenomenon of the blind or paralyzed person suddenly restored to health by personal suggestion or by a shock of some kind has always intrigued the imagination.

During the nineteenth century a good deal of work was done in treating conversion patients by means of hypnosis. These patients, tending to be suggestible, make ready subjects for the hypnotist and it is possible often to modify or eliminate their symptoms by suggestions of cure made during the hypnotic state. Also, the physicians of the last century were gratified to observe that some of these patients when hypnotized were able to recall and to recount incidents which had a direct bearing on their symptoms. These phenomena are of great significance, not so much from the standpoint of the individual under treatment, but rather as observations of psychodynamics.

To the neurologist of the early days a conversion symptom "didn't make sense." Here was, for example, an anesthesia of an arm. The person could be burned or pricked over the involved area with no show of pain, yet the nerves and skin were intact and might in fact be responding normally the next day. Neither did the involvement follow the distribution of any specific nerves but rather was determined by the patient's "idea" of his arm as comprising everything from fingertips to shoulder. The patients were for the most part relatively calm and outwardly free from emotional disturbance. They showed "la belle indifference," as Charcot phrased it. The conversion symptom appeared to be an effect without a cause.

Studies of these patients under hypnosis established the fact that their symptoms did have a cause; that this cause was a state of conflict of which they were unaware. They had *converted* the problem into a symptom, thus dissociating it from consciousness and having no anxiety about it. This interpretation led, for the first time in medical history, to a systematic study of the role of the unconscious in relation to neurotic symptoms and provided the foundation for our present-day acceptance of a meaning and purpose in these symptoms.

Although conversion hysteria does not occur exclusively in women, it does represent a blocking in normal sexual development, with a displacement of sexuality to organs other than the genitals. Some symptoms seem frankly to express a substitutive sexual act, as, for example, in the obviously erotic movements in some hysterical convulsive states. In other cases the purpose seems to be increased repression, as in episodes of blindness or mutism related to guilt-provoking sights or unacceptable words.

The typical conflict revealed by studies of conversion hysteria patients is that of repression of adult sexual feeling because of the guilt and confusion related to this feeling in early childhood. The patient usually avoids sexual experience or accepts it with revulsion or serious conflict. Often it is observed that a sexual experience or the fear of one precipitates the onset of symptoms. A tendency to conversion symptoms in patients of this type, however, makes them vulnerable to react in this way to other situations of stress and strain which seem, directly at least, unrelated to sexuality.

The particular organ affected by a conversion symptom may be determined by its symbolic meaning or by more casual circumstances that associate it with the patient's conflict. It is sometimes observed that organs weakened by illness or surgery are more susceptible to involvement. Hysterical mutism may follow a tonsillectomy, for example, or paralysis of the legs occur after a minor industrial accident. In these cases a longing for dependency (to avoid a mature sexual life and also to secure financial compensation!) may create a complicated situation.

Mass manifestations of conversion hysteria are less prevalent now but were apparently rather common in the last century. Neurologists of the time described the spread of such symptoms as convulsive states through hospital wards. The symptoms were determined in this case by suggestion.

The symptoms of conversion hysteria can often be cleared up by strong suggestion given either during hypnosis or in relation to some procedure (such as an electric shock) which is accompanied by reassurance of cure. However, such symptomatic treatment does not cure the underlying emotional problem and symptoms eliminated in such ways tend to recur, or to be followed by other conversions. Therapy must be aimed basically toward the patient's sexual maturation. Inhibiting conflicts must be brought into consciousness and resolved in a mature and realistic way. Unless this is accomplished a true cure is not effected, although a compromise may be reached by which the patient adjusts to his sexual immaturity in a way of life that makes allowance for it.

Compulsive-Obsessive Neurosis

The phobic and conversion neuroses tend usually to be fairly well circumscribed; that is, they are not completely interwoven with the patient's character structure. *Compulsive-obsessive neurosis,* on the other hand, is more clearly an exaggeration of basic attitudes. Its symptoms represent a caricature of the ambivalent drives related to conformity versus rebellion—those conflicting attitudes which we have seen as beginning in the toilet training period, and when persistent crystallizing into typical anal character. They produce the person who is precise, formalistic, and often moralistic, who relies on these strong defenses of conformity to defend himself against the repressed rebellion, hostility, and guilt with which he cannot deal. This type of character illustrates the result of too rigid repression—a personality outwardly correct to excess but unable to deviate from his set pattern without anxiety. He does not necessarily develop the symptoms of a neurosis but leads a relatively restricted life because of his lack of flexibility and his inability to react freely and generously with other people.

When a person of anal character is confronted with a situation conducive to breakdown—that is, one which strengthens the repressed or weakens repression—he may develop the bizarre symptoms of a compulsive-obsessive neurosis. In these symptoms he expresses symbolically his forbidden tendencies and/or his defenses against them.

Compulsions and obsessions have a wide variety of forms but in general are related to guilt or to hostility. One common compulsive symptom is the need constantly to wash the hands, associated with a good deal of anxiety about dirt in general. The feeling back of this compulsion is one of contamination, but the patient is not aware of its meaning in terms of his repressed "dirty" impulses. Ritualistic activities preoccupy the compulsive patient. He must arrange and rearrange his belongings, put on his clothes in a particular order, tap on the chair before sitting down, walk always with hands in pockets, and the like. All these symptoms are exaggerated ways of being orderly, neat, and systematic. The obsessive patient is subject to recurrent thoughts of a kind that distresses and puzzles him. They have to do always with ideas unacceptable to his ego, such as the thought of murdering or otherwise harming someone —often a member of the family. One of the most frequent and distressing obsessions is the parent's idea of harming his or her child.

Obsessive-compulsive neurosis in severe forms is an extremely handicapping state. The person is compelled to spend much of his day in routines which he recognizes as irrational but cannot control. Any attempts to restrict these activities throw him into intense anxiety, yet the persistence in the routine does not give him peace of mind. He is driven by forces in himself which he denounces yet must obey. He admits the bizarre nature of his behavior, even asks for help to be relieved of it. Aside from the compulsive situation he is in touch with reality and is a rational human being. If his symptoms are obsessive thoughts rather than compulsive acts he gives less outward show of deviation, but he lives in a state of torment. The ideas which obsess him are repulsive to his conscious self. Often he fears (though he need not) that he will act out the terrible fantasies. One patient, for example, told of obsessions that began with the idea that she might kill her sister, cut her up, and throw her into the toilet. Similar ideas attached themselves over the years to her husband and others more casually related. Such ideas may be vaguely persistent constantly or may occur only occasionally.

The dividing line is not sharp between a clear-cut neurosis of this type and the less dominating compulsive-obsessive components prevalent in human behavior. We see ritualistic tendencies frequently in children and a kind of obsessive quality marks the common superstitions. "Step on a crack, break your mother's back; spilled salt is bad luck—throw some over the left shoulder; say 'Gesundheit' if someone sneezes; avoid room thirteen"; we could go on with many more. All these relatively casual and only half-believed concepts are expressive of man's insecurity and his irrational attempts to build concrete defenses against threatening forces within himself and in the outside world. The distinction between pathologic and nonpathologic here, as elsewhere in psychiatry, is quantitative. When the repressed and hence nonintegrated forces within a personality are reinforced to the point where they threaten to break through and deny the person's concept of himself and when that concept is too rigidly established to bear modification, then the unacceptable impulses come out in a distorted way. Under these circumstances the patient can rightly say, "These are no part of me; this is imposed on me against my will." It is true that the patient does not wish to cut up her sister; by caricaturing her resentment of her sister and reacting to it with terror she denies the real fact of her strongly hostile attitude toward the sister and toward anyone who competes and makes demands. The patient dedicated to a continuous ritual does not recognize his need for absolute exactness as a check on his wish to behave as a little child untrained in obedience.

It would have been better if these patients had accomplished their socialization in a more flexible, less intimidated way. They have developed strong and punitive superegos which make it difficult for them to accept the unrighteous elements in themselves. Because of this blocking they resist attempts to analyze the conflict—throwing up against such attempts a wordy barrage of denials of evil. Even when they conscientiously attempt therapy, repression has done its work so well that the nature of the conflicts becomes apparent to them only after long periods of exploration and reassurance.

The less well-established symptoms of compulsive-obsessive nature are, of course, more easily treated. They are often seen as transitory expressions of disturbance in response to increased strain, subsiding under more favorable circumstances or with the help of a supportive yet frank therapeutic approach.

All the neurotic conditions which we have described are in whole or in part defenses against tendencies unacceptable to the patient's own ego. Being unrecognized consciously, these tendencies must be defended against blindly in the form of symptoms that seriously interfere with the patient's efficiency and his capacity for pleasure in life. There is little gratification in neurotic symptoms, though the patient may derive from them some element of gain in the way of a dependent, protected situation.

The Unrestrained Impulse

In another kind of neurosis we see a different solution of conflict: one by which the unacceptable impulses are expressed directly, breaking through the ego-superego barriers in an inexorable, repetitious way, apparently beyond control of the patient himself. They take the form of behavior which differs from other neurotic behavior in having a pleasurable quality about it, a primitive satisfaction of a sort ordinarily subject to social restraint.

This direct expression of unsocialized impulse may be limited to certain acts highly charged with emotion and symbolic significance. This circumscribed form of *Impulse Neurosis* is illustrated by such conditions as kleptomania and pyromania and certain sexual deviations such as voyeurism (peeping) and exhibitionism. All these acts are pleasurable to the person concerned. He recognizes them, however, as undesirable behavior, but is unable to control them. He even may act in such a way as to assure his being apprehended and punished—motivated by his sense of guilt. But his knowledge of wrongdoing does not protect him against recurrence.

Study of the impulse neurosis reveals particularly well the interesting tendency of the unconscious to express itself in symbols. Just as anyone in his dreams of fire expresses violence, destructiveness, sexual passion, so the fire-setting patient expresses in his acting-out way the violent content of his unconscious. The kleptomaniac feels impelled to collect articles which have no practical value to him. The motivating drive is his unconscious longing for that which belongs to someone else. His stealing gratifies the longing temporarily, but since it gives him not what he really wants but only a symbol of it, his equilibrium is of short duration. The repressed needs which motivate these impulsive acts are infantile ones, such as a longing for exclusive possession of the mother or early-inhibited violent rage against a parent. Kleptomania and pyromania, therefore, frequently occur in childhood. The conflict may be activated in later life as a regressive turning away from increasing responsibility and social restrictions. Similarly the sexual impulsive acts are relics of the early childish need of the boy to satisfy his curiosities or assuage his castration anxieties.

The Alcoholic Neurosis

Another group of neurotic conditions representing essentially an impulsive acting out to relieve tension consists of the various addictions. Alcoholism may be observed as representative of this group. All addictions follow a similar pattern, though with differences superimposed by the effects of the respective drugs.

Alcoholism we may define as a neurosis characterized by the compulsive, repetitive use of alcohol for satisfaction of basic personality needs, the alcohol becoming progressively more of a substitute for the realistic, socially integrated satisfaction of these needs. The distinction of neurotic alcoholism from so-called social drinking lies in the more compulsive use of the drug and its use increasingly as a substitute for other satisfactions rather than merely as a reinforcement of them.

The psychodynamics of alcoholism are those of the impulse neurosis in that the person follows an impulse to the attainment of pleasure (or at least relief of suffering) directly. The drive to drink, like the drive of the kleptomaniac to steal, has about it an irresistible quality. The chronic alcoholic patient finds it as difficult to give up his symptom by merely deciding to do so as the phobic patient would find it difficult to overcome his phobia by an act of will.

The traits of character which predispose to alcoholism are those we have discussed as oral traits. In addition the alcoholic, like all impulsive neurotics, shows a lowered capacity for tolerance of tensions. In other words, he is a person with strong needs for "taking in" rather than "giving out" and he reacts excessively in situations which thwart his needs for reassurance and support. He may usually be recognized as basically a passive receptive person, however much he may have covered these characteristics by an aggressive façade. In alcohol he seems to find an easy road to comfort. "It makes me feel good." In addition to giving an immediate sense of oral gratification, the alcohol paralyzes the areas of the brain which are concerned with higher mental functions: guilt, inhibitions, moral concepts. It is, indeed, quite apropos to define superego as the alcohol-soluble part of the personality! With this troublesome aspect removed, one is relatively free of guilt and conflict and may establish, though with some sense of uneasiness, a sense of well-being, of power and satisfaction in the world.

Unfortunately for the alcoholic, he becomes involved in vicious circles which make more and more difficult for him a realistic social adjustment. As he drinks to overcome guilt and shame, he progressively loses prestige and self-esteem and therefore must drink more to compensate. Also, since he uses alcohol as a substitute for other satisfactions, he contributes little to his environment, hence little is given to him and he finds himself in a vicious circle of failure, retreat into alcohol, and increasing failure. This failure involves everything in his life: love, sexual gratification, friendship, work achievement. The weakening of interpersonal relationships widens the schism between the patient and the outer world and thus weakens the ego by depriving it further of its function of social integration. As failure in all areas of activity becomes more obvious, the patient drifts toward the psychotic way of changing reality to fit his own needs. His drift toward psychosis is facilitated by the destructive effects of the alcohol itself on the brain.

Because of the dependent passive quality of the alcoholic character, treatment of this condition is most efficient if it offers a strong, supportive, and reassuring contact. The organization called Alcoholics Anonymous presents what seems to be a most successful approach to this problem. The patient feels understood and protected within the organization and is aware of the strength and solidarity of the group behind him as he attempts to win their praise by good performance. The continuity of influence offered by such a group is important, as is the warm personal and religious quality of the rapport between members.

Impulsive neurotic patients who have limited the expression of their unsocial impulses to certain repetitious acts may function otherwise in a socially integrated way. One might consider that the repressing capacity has in these cases broken down only in relation to one particularly strong impulse. Otherwise ego and superego standards continue to influence to a normal degree the patient's social behavior. This is true of such monosymptomatic patients as the kleptomaniac and exhibitionist, and the early alcoholic. The addict of any kind, however, because of the destructive character of his behavior patterns and the damaging effects of the drugs he uses, soon becomes more totally involved.

Psychopathic Personality

When the breaking through of primitive impulse is not circumscribed but involves the patient's behavior in general, the result is the neurosis known as *psychopathic personality*. Here the repressed is no longer repressed but manifests itself in the patient's most basic dealings with his fellow-men. The so-called psychopath is one who from early childhood has been unreliable and irresponsible in his interpersonal relationships. He steals, lies, breaks his promises, even in some cases kills. He may express an understanding of the fact that his acts are wrong and may vow repentance but his words, and apparently even his conscious intentions, do not prevent a repetition of the antisocial behavior.

The psychopath differs from the nonneurotic delinquent person by the less realistic nature of the psychopath's behavior. His antisocial acts have an impulsive, relatively purposeless character, repeated in situations which seem not to provoke them, even in situations which obviously expose the psychopath to detection and punishment. There is in fact a tendency in many such persons to seek punishment at regular intervals. It is as though the patient's own superego is too weak to control his id-motivated behavior but manages to insure punishment once the deed is done. He seldom enjoys the gains of his aggression. Whereas another person might steal because he needs money or because it is the tradition of his group, the psychopath steals for the sake of stealing. If he kills it is seldom a crime of vengeance or passion but a blind and unmotivated act on the impulse of the moment.

It is obvious that psychopathic personality is related to defects in superego development. The early manifestation of this lack has led to a concept of this disorder as a constitutionally deficient state, and it has been labeled "constitutional psychopathic state" and "moral imbecility." However, as interest is directed more to the genetics of neurotic disorder, away from a mere description of it, one is impressed by the close relationship of psychopathic patterns to the early environmental situation of the patient. It would be hard to conceive of moral and social attitudes as inherited, like intellectual capacity. These attitudes represent one's concept of how people live together, a concept certainly determined by the experiences which the person has had in the early years of his life. There are, to be sure, innate differences in adaptive capacity. Frustrating, depriving situations to which one might react with psychopathic traits might cause a less serious maladjustment in another person. Granting this, we still see the psychopath as having failed to integrate a satisfactory social code because he could not identify with the authoritative figures in his world who represented that code. The child's moral sense—his superego— is taken over from his parents or their surrogates. If the attitude between his parents and himself is one of deep distrust and hostility he may accept their mores only as external regulating authority, never as an integrated part of his character structure.

The diagnosis of psychopathic personality is often of importance legally. It implies that the criminal is not psychotic and hence is responsible for his behavior, having the ability to distinguish right from wrong.

It is true that the psychopath is intellectually cognizant of the fact that his behavior is wrong. Any resolutions of reform which he may make on the basis of this understanding are, however, unreliable. His character structure is such that his acts are motivated directly by impulse, the usual ego-superego codes and understandings being incapable of influencing these acts.

Treatment of this condition is obviously difficult and often must be determined by the welfare of society rather than by that of the patient himself. Punishment only acts to increase hostility or assuage guilt, in either case predisposing to further antisocial activity. Appeals to morality and social responsibility are useless in view of the impotence of ego and superego to control behavior. The type of therapy which has at times been effective relies on a gradual building up of superego on the basis of the patient's acceptance of the therapist. Superego represents a taking over into one's self of the code of behavior of a parent figure. A defective superego indicates, therefore, that the patient's early relationships with parent figures were so unsatisfactory that he rejected the socialization which they attempted to impose on him. The therapist can succeed only if he becomes to the patient a more acceptable person in a relationship of genuine trust and admiration. From him the patient can then accept, as he could not from his own parents, the standards of social living, and can gradually make these standards a part of his own functioning. Obviously the opportunities are rare for such patient and long continued therapeutic relationships.

Neurotic Depression

Before going on to a discussion of the psychoses, we should mention briefly a condition which seems symptomatically to resemble one of the major psychoses. This is the syndrome known as *neurotic depression* or reactive depression. An analysis of this condition provides an opportunity for bringing out distinctions between the neurotic and the psychotic adaptive mechanisms.

Depression is a quality of functioning with which everyone is familiar. It is normal in so far as it is a logical response to an unfavorable life situation. One is realistically depressed by loss of a loved one, by a serious failure of achievement, by the observation of tragedy or the experience of it. The reactions are related quantitatively to the severity of the precipitating situation and tend to clear up as the situation is overcome or as one reconciles one's self to it.

Neurotic depression differs from so-called normal depression in that the depth and persistence of the reaction are out of proportion to the precipitating cause. There may in fact be no clear-cut external cause. We see, for example, a student becoming inordinately depressed after failure in an examination. He loses appetite, feels slowed up and disinterested in his former activities, develops an extreme sense of inadequacy. He recognizes his feelings as out of proportion and unreasonable, yet cannot pull himself out of the "slough of despond." Obviously he is reacting not merely to his immediate failure but to this failure as symbolizing the rejecting and too demanding world. A deep sense of unacceptability may be well compensated for as long as one is relatively successful, but any failure breaks down the defense and makes evident the unstable foundations of self-confidence. The term *reactive depression* covers such excessive reactions to realistically frustrating circumstances. Neurotic depression may occur, however, where no such circumstance is recognizable and where the patient's symptoms represent a cumulative sense of dissatisfaction with himself and his environment.

The symptoms of neurotic depression are similar to those of anxiety state in that they present a generally disorganized and unhappy state of physical and psychic functioning. They differ in the quality of the mood, which is one of sadness, disinterest, and pessimism in the depressed patient, in contrast to the fearfulness of the anxiety patient. In each case the patient finds mental concentration difficult and is distressed by his inability to enjoy the pleasurable aspects of his life. Food, sex, friendship, aesthetic stimulation leave him relatively unresponsive and he often describes himself as feeling "dead." His ideas are monotonously concerned with his own unhappy state. Feeling unwanted, he tends to withdraw from social contacts. He functions outwardly, however, with more efficiency than he feels. His activities may lack spontaneity and initiative but ordinarily he is able to continue with them.

Neurotic depression is a relatively benign condition and in many cases it is a transient state which clears up spontaneously. If it is based on severe conflicts it may of course indicate the patient's vulnerability to stress and strain, which makes recurrence of such episodes likely, or predisposes to a chronically depressed outlook. The patient who can be helped to deal frankly with the repressed conflictual elements in his character structure has a good chance of overcoming his depressive tendencies.

The symptoms of neurotic depression appear to differ only in degree from those of psychotic depression. In both states there is the loss of capacity for pleasure, the general retardation of activity, the monotonous self-related pessimism of ideas. The difference, however, is qualitative as well as quantitative in that the neurotic patient does not distort reality to fit his mood as does the psychotic patient. This is the line of demarcation—though not always indeed too sharply drawn—between the inefficient and unrealistic reactions which we have been observing so far, and the adaptations by distortion and denial to which we shall next direct our attention.

chapter 9

ADAPTATION BY DISTORTION AND DENIAL: Psychosis

> Now see that noble and most sovereign reason
> Like sweet bells jangled, out of tune and harsh.
> —William Shakespeare: *Hamlet*

W<small>E MAY</small> think of neurosis in its various forms as a limited kind of functioning. The neurotic conflict absorbs a certain greater or lesser amount of adaptive energy, which is thus diverted from more realistic and efficient action, and remains bound up in the repetitive-compulsive pattern of the neurosis. Outside the area of the symptoms, however, the neurotic person deals frankly with reality. His attitude toward himself and his life situation remains, according to universal human standards, realistic.

P<small>SYCHOTIC</small> B<small>REAKDOWN</small>

As we turn from neurosis to psychosis, we find ourselves dealing with very different phenomena. In psychosis the patient does not make a partial adaptation to his situation.

Instead, he capitulates. His ego, which has the function of appraising his world, no longer fulfills that function but ignores or is unable to perceive facts, reconstructing instead a reality of distortion and denial. The ego function concerned with internal integration also breaks down, allowing dissociation of personality components. These disorganizations of the personality in its internal and external relationships are so extreme that it is difficult to make contact with the psychotic patient. We can no longer easily establish a common perspective with him; the abyss is deep and wide.

Distortion and denial are to be sure not exclusively psychotic traits. Everyone sees the world with a hopeful or discouraging aspect, depending to a large extent on his mood of the moment. Fantasy is a common refuge or defense and we have already seen that common paranoid projections may approach close to a delusional state. The distinction of psychotic from nonpsychotic is, however, both a quantitative and a qualitative one. It is measured by the degree of ego involvement and by the kind of attitude the person has toward his own symptoms. The nonpsychotic person judges his symptoms by the generally accepted standards of reality. The psychotic person judges reality according to his symptoms. This distinction will become clearer as we examine the specific psychoses.

It is an interesting and really surprising fact that psychotic symptoms can be classified into only three clinical syndromes: The manic-depressive, the schizophrenic, and the paranoid. This perhaps is another indication of the similarity of mental processes in all human beings. In states of extreme disturbance of the total personality there emerges an exaggeration of mood, a withdrawal into fantasy, or a set of delusions of persecution.

Toward More Constructive Attitudes

It is only relatively recently that classification of and rational approach to these disorders has been attempted. Earlier in history the madman, the fool, or the one possessed was regarded as evil or the victim of evil, incomprehensible to the normal mind and untreatable. They were allowed to roam at will or were confined by brutal methods. Within the last hundred years, three trends have converged into the more constructive attitudes of present-day psychiatry.*

The first of these trends was expressed in the rise of a humanitarian concept which stressed the beneficial effects on the so-called lunatic of kind and sympathetic treatment. The pioneers in this field insisted on the right of psychotic patients to be treated as human beings; they deplored the ridicule and abuse which were meted out to these unfortunate and helpless persons.

The second trend was a more scientific, medical approach to psychiatric problems. Emphasis was put on the role of the organically damaged brain, and attempts were made to establish a correlation between psychotic symptoms and nervous system disease. Such a correlation could be established in the case of the organic dementias, with the result that some of these conditions were given the benefit of specific treatment. Even where no clear-cut correlation was demonstrable, the medical approach, which favored careful and systematic observations, began to bring order into chaos by setting apart syndromes of symptoms and establishing a basis for classification. Although at present it seems preferable to regard psychosis as a total personality reaction

---

* See G. Zilboorg, *A History of Medical Psychology* (New York: W. W. Norton & Co., Inc., 1941).

rather than simply a product of neurological damage, yet the medical approach continues to make a large contribution to psychiatric understanding.

The third approach might be called the psychodynamic. It is based on the idea that psychiatric disorders are neither incomprehensible quirks of fate nor simply the result of a weak or damaged brain. Instead it sees even the most bizarre symptoms as products of circumstances, of cause and effect. These symptoms have a meaning in terms of the patient's life history, and in many cases they can be seen to have a purpose for him. The concept of a mentally disordered state as *dynamic* implies an activity, a state of striving, a kind of attempt at working out a problem. This is in contrast to the static concept of psychiatric symptoms as peculiar deviations which exist for no reason, dissociated from the patient's life history or present state of social adaptation.

The Psychodynamic Approach

The psychodynamic point of view has developed rapidly within the past decade. It is a product of accumulating observations of the fact that man's internal conflicts may express themselves in strange and symbolic ways. Interest focuses not merely on the patient's present state but on the way this state has developed out of experiences that preceded it. A psychotic delusion may in itself seem incongruous, but viewed against the background of the patient's experiences it can be seen as an understandable process—as a kind of adaptation. Emphasis therefore is placed on the history of the patient's breakdown, rather than merely on a description of his symptoms. Its beginnings are seen in early life patterns, in the accumulation of failures and frustrations which tax adaptive capacity to the point of disorganization.*

Psychotic symptoms themselves present a challenge for understanding not only of the patient but of human functioning in general. Their meaning is less readily accessible than is that of the neuroses because once a psychosis is fully developed the patient does not cooperate well with attempts to study him. His symptoms serve often, in fact, as a defense against self-understanding or self-revelation. With patience and persistence, however, one may to a varying degree comprehend the meaning of his language and his mood. When it is possible to establish contact with a patient during the period of transition into psychosis much often can be accomplished. Frequently one observes at this time the vacillation between realistic interpretation and flight into psychosis. A delusion, for example, will be tentatively held. "Maybe it's just my idea," or "Maybe I'm too sensitive." A dramatic example of this vacillation was expressed by a young boy with early schizophrenic symptoms who said, "I could be king over thousands of people but I don't want to be; I'm just a little boy. Take this thing out of me!" **

Psychotic Depression

In distinguishing between neurotic and psychotic reactions we have briefly mentioned the condition known as *psychotic depression*. This is a state of overwhelming involvement in self-disparaging and world-disparaging attitudes, which greatly restricts and distorts the patient's con-

---

* See Paul Federn, *Ego Psychology and the Psychoses* (New York: Basic Books, Inc., 1952).

** B. C. Bosselman, *Psychiatric Quarterly*, XIX (April, 1945).

cepts. He no longer sees himself and his environment as others would see them, but makes interpretation in keeping with his mood. "I am a hopeless sinner," "Everything is useless," "The world is punishing me, torturing me," and the like.

Manic-Depressive Psychosis

The most clearly recognized and described syndrome of psychotic depression is that which alternates with excitement in the disorder known as *manic-depressive psychosis*. This is a psychosis which occurs in episodes of depressive or excited states. One patient may have during his lifetime several spells of depression only or of excitement only, or may show a tendency to alternate between these extremes. Usually recovery from an episode is complete; the patient shows no indication of permanent damage. A disturbed episode, untreated, has a duration of six months to a year in most cases.

Manic-depressive episodes are rare in childhood, though they do occasionally occur, especially in the preadolescent years. The typical age of onset is early maturity. Recurrence is common but it is not inevitable. The severity of the condition varies widely. Some patients have only one manic or depressive period in a lifetime, others may have two or three widely spaced, with good adjustment between them. The more seriously involved patient passes from one episode into another or settles down into a chronically depressed state.

There is apparently a hereditary predisposition to manic-depressive psychosis, though this cannot be established in all cases. In some patients the inexorable occurrence of the swings which seem unrelated to experience suggests either a constitutional or an early developed vulnerability; in others the episodes can be clearly related to difficult life circumstances. It is again a question of interaction involving native adaptive capacity, early established character patterns, and the nature of the later life situation.

A characteristic feature of manic-depressive psychosis is its consistency. One observes that all the symptoms of the depressed patient express his mood. His physiological functions are retarded; he moves slowly, speaks hesitatingly. His thought processes are restricted and ideas follow the monotonous theme of unworthiness and hopelessness. The manic patient in contrast is constantly moving about, talking rapidly and incessantly, laughing, shouting, and singing. His mind flits from one idea to another; he is distractible, flighty, and apparently elated. The most severely depressed patient sits about in a state resembling stupor, or paces the floor in great agitation. The extremely manic patient exhausts himself with his excitement.

This consistency of manic or depressive symptoms is indicative of an interesting and unique phenomenon. In this psychosis we see personality dominated by one of its elements. In a depressive state superego controls; in a manic state the symptoms express id impulses. This means that the manic-depressive breakdown is essentially a failure in the ego function of preserving internal harmony.

Ego has been described as the integrating aspect of personality which serves two purposes: first, to perceive external reality and adapt the person to it, and second, to preserve harmony internally by integrating the id demands with the moral code of the superego. This latter function is the one which breaks down in manic-depressive psychosis. We must assume, therefore, that in this condition the ego is relatively weak and that id or superego or both are strong.

The person who repeatedly becomes depressed is subjecting himself to punishment by his own rigid, sadistic superego. The need for punishment, which he expresses in his constant fantasies of guilt and unworthiness, results from id impulses with which his ego cannot deal. These impulses are for the most part unacknowledged and unrecognized by the patient. They take the form of delusions of great sin or fasten themselves on trivial incidents. One woman, for example, when depressed insisted she was being punished for having accidentally dropped a baby ten years before. The delusion of the unforgivable sin is common in severe depression. The hostile impulses about which the person is actually guilty are not frankly expressed, but may be observed in the deep sense of anger which he expresses mostly about himself but which come out also toward the world generally. The more closely one observes a depressed patient the more clearly one senses the hostility which he covers with self-abnegation.

The manic patient asserts a great sense of freedom from restraint. "I'm having a fling for once," one patient said. His previous superego codes are flaunted. His symptoms express particularly those attitudes which are ordinarily subject to repression. He is exhibitionistic, bold, arrogant, sexually promiscuous. In the mild cases or in early stages of the disorder it may have been observed that the person was behaving more rashly than usual, spending money freely, talking and laughing loudly, showing less than his previous sexual inhibition. This state is described as "hypomanic." It may go on into a frank manic state or may clear up without more serious difficulty.

The failure of the internal integrating function of the ego in manic-depressive state indicates as we have observed, a relatively weak ego. Obviously it is, however, strong enough to preserve integration during much of the patient's lifetime; it fails only at intervals when presumably conflicts have accumulated to the breaking point. This vulnerability of the ego seems to be related to the fact (which has been repeatedly observed in the study of these patients) that the character structure has a strongly oral quality.

The oral character has been described as having a greedy, demanding quality. Much reassurance and sustenance are needed; the person lacks a sense of inner strength and must draw on those about him for emotional support. Such a dependent, demanding attitude often leads to difficulty, inasmuch as the person who takes a great deal tends to meet with rejection. The rejection increases his demands and then a vicious circle is developed. If the strongly oral person is fortunate enough to have generous and supportive people about him who do not impose severe demands, he needs not break down. Certainly orality is common in human character structure and only a small proportion of people with this trait develop a psychosis.

Another factor which makes the oral person more vulnerable to breakdown is an ambivalent attitude, that is, a marked tendency to struggle between moral codes and primitive drives. This was implied in the observation that both id and superego components were relatively strong. Drives for direct gratification conflict with a rigid moral concept; between them the ego is unable to compromise.

This, then, seems to be the background for a manic-depressive psychosis: a person essentially receptive, needing much emotional support and reassurance from the external world, must at the same time reconcile within himself a strong moral code and a powerful drive for direct gratification. The breakdown may be the result of experiences that suddenly increase the difficulties or it may be the result of an accumulative sense of frustration. Whether the patient develops depression or a manic state depends on the relative strength of superego and id.

The ego function which adapts to external reality does not collapse in this condition as completely as it does, as we shall see later, in schizophrenia. The patient does, however, distort reality to fit his mood. He perceives its realities but colors them by his depressed or manic fantasies. Perhaps because the patient's hold on reality is not completely lost, he tends to recover without damage from a manic-depressive episode. He seems to act out something with his symptoms —to do penance in depression or to indulge in an orgy of self-expression in the manic mood. After this the ego gradually again assumes control.

Treatment

Recovery of the severely depressed patient is hastened by shock treatment.* This consists of a series of artifically produced convulsive seizures, spaced at intervals of several days. It is a form of treatment which in recent years has been loosely and often unwisely used for many psychiatric conditions. The one disorder for which it is specifically useful appears to be depression. We can at present only theorize about the meaning of this result. It may act as a punitive measure, thus satisfying the excessive superego demands; it may tend to mobilize the life forces by threat of annihilation, or it may have some physiologic effect on the brain areas concerned in the patient's conflict. At any rate it

---

* L. B. Kalinowsky and P. H. Hoch, *Shock Treatments, Psychosurgery and Other Somatic Procedures in Psychiatry* (New York: Grune & Stratton, Inc., 1952).

seems to be indicated for alleviating and sometimes overcoming the prolonged suffering of the depressed person. It is seldom as effective in manic states, though it may quiet the excitement to some degree.

The milder manic or depressive states usually react well to a treatment program of supportive medical care. Caution must be observed, however, in respect to the possibilities of suicide by the depressed patient. Suicidal ideas are common in this state and would frequently be acted on if the patient were not protected against self-destruction. This is not surprising in view of the patient's suffering, his lack of interest in anything, and his depreciation both of himself and of the world about him.

Psychotherapy—that is, the attempt to alleviate disturbing symptoms by establishing a constructive patient-therapist relationship—is of limited value in manic-depressive psychosis. While the patient is severely involved he cannot be reached. His repetitious ideas of guilt, his flighty impulsiveness—both act as barriers to rapport. Reassurance of the depressed person or logical reasoning with the manic either tends to intensify the symptoms or is completely ignored. Therapy after recovery would seem to be indicated for prevention of recurrence, but few of these patients seem interested in it. Once free of symptoms they turn away again from their inner conflicts, assuming that all will be well. Those who are willing and able to undertake intensive therapy should be encouraged in this as the most effective approach to their problem. It is important, however, that the therapist be aware of the limits of the patient's ego strength in dealing with his oral needs and his strong internal struggles. A supportive and reassuring though frank attitude on the part of the therapist is probably of greatest value here.

Involutional Melancholia

Depression of mood is a common human reaction to difficulty. We have observed in reactive depression an exaggerated neurotic response to frustration. Depression also is a predominant symptom in psychoses other than the manic-depressive state. The psychosis occurring in the involutional period, known as *involutional melancholia*, may resemble closely a manic-depressive depression. The symptoms are, however, often intermixed with others of a schizophrenic or paranoid nature.

Involutional psychosis occurs in women of about fifty, and in men of about sixty. It seems to represent a reaction against the loss of previous opportunities for self-expression and gratification. The man feels less effective and less well accepted in his work; the woman senses a loss of significance as her attractiveness is diminished and as her children no longer depend on her. Physiologic changes are no doubt involved, though no specific hormonal state can be observed to be directly related. When the psychosis is predominantly a depression its symptoms may be indistinguishable from those of manic-depressive psychosis, and one looks for a history of previous upsets to determine the diagnosis. The treatment and prognosis in either case are similar though it has been observed that an involutional depression untreated tends to persist longer than an untreated manic-depressive episode. In cases where symptoms are mixed with paranoid and schizophrenic elements, the outlook is more complicated though there is a fair rate of recovery.

Treatment of the involutional psychosis by shock therapy has favorable results in most cases. This should be followed by a form of psychotherapy which attempts to renew the patient's courage and which helps him to adjust to the changing life situation. A more intensive, analytic approach is usually not indicated. The stirring up of old conflicts involved in such a process usually does more harm than good at this time of life.

Manic-depressive depression and involutional melancholia are psychoses of relatively frequent occurrence. The depressive syndrome may also express itself, though usually not consistently, in organic brain disease, as we shall observe later.

Schizophrenia

When manic-depressive psychosis was first named and described by the German psychiatrist Kraepelin [*] in the latter part of the last century, it was contrasted with another group of disorders which Kraepelin called *dementia praecox*. This condition tends to manifest itself earlier in life (*praecox*—youth), and Kraepelin believed that it culminated in dementia. Although it is no longer thought of as a dementing disorder, it is a malignant type of psychosis with a recovery rate of only about 15 per cent. The name *dementia praecox* has been largely replaced by that of schizophrenia (split mind) applied by Bleuler [**] to describe the characteristic splitting of functions observed in this psychosis.

Schizophrenia accounts for about 19 per cent of all first admissions to state hospitals, and being a chronic disabling disease it makes up a large part of the hospital's population. Within this diagnostic group is a number of subgroups, differing a great deal in outward symptomatology but having in common the essential schizophrenic pattern. This pat-

[*] Emil Kraepelin, *Clinical Psychiatry* (Leipzig, 1913).
[**] Eugen Bleuler, *Dementia Praecox oder Gruppe der Schizophrenia* (Leipzig, 1911).

tern might be concisely stated as first, a denial and disregard of objective reality, and second, a reconstruction through fantasy of a delusional and hallucinatory replacement of reality.

The reality denials of the schizophrenic patient represent the most extreme degree of ego failure. This patient, unable to cope with his adaptive problems, denies that they exist. His ego relinquishes its perceptive function and no longer makes contact with the objective world. Interest is focused within and the patient lives, we say, autistically, in fantasy rather than in reality.

Many symptoms of the psychosis are expressions of this withdrawn state. The patient's language, for example, is often unintelligible, his emotional attitude toward his environment detached and apathetic. He ordinarily shows no interest in communicating with people around him, talking not for purposes of conversation but only to express involvement in his fantasies. The understanding listener may in time be able to translate much of the apparent babbling into concepts that have a good deal of meaning in relation to the patient's problems. One woman, aged twenty-nine, said when asked her age, "I'm thirteen—thirteen—twenty-nine. Half of me is thirteen and half is twenty-nine." Sometimes a patient will give unconcerned and facetious answers to questions, later revealing the fact that he could have answered correctly had he any motive for doing so. A man made whimsical responses when asked the date but later in the conversation expressed a wish to go home for Christmas and when asked how long it was until Christmas answered precisely. It seems that the unintelligible speech represents not a defect in ability to communicate but a lack of any incentive to do so, a result of the patient's detachment from the outside world.

The "flatness" of mood of the schizophrenic patient would be expected in view of his lack of responsiveness to external stimuli. He appears indifferent, apathetic. The feelings which he does—sometimes violently—express show no relationship to his surroundings but relate rather to his delusional-hallucinatory experiences.

The characterization of this psychosis on the basis of the "split mind" has led to much popular and erroneous use of the concept. The term *split* is used to describe anything from a conscious state of conflict to hysterical dissociated states. Bleuler, who coined the term *schizophrenia*, applied it to describe the lack of integration of the patient's functions. It may be observed, for example, that a patient complains of being tortured but meanwhile smiles or appears emotionally unconcerned. He states that he is the King of England but makes no protest against waiting on tables in the hospital. There is thus a kind of fragmentation of his activities, a lack of any consistent organization. This too is understandable in view of his loss of the perceptive and integrative function of the ego. Objective facts and goals no longer motivate him; his behavior is determined by the shifting whims of his fantasy.

This lack of consistency in symptoms is one of the outstanding distinctions between this psychosis and the manic-depressive state. We observed in the latter condition that all the personality functions—ideation, emotion, physical activity, expressed the patient's mood of depression or elation. Here in contrast the patient is self-contradictory, apparently chaotic in his personality organization. The break with reality is more complete in the schizophrenic because, as we have already observed, he has lost the perceptive function of the ego—that most basic capacity for establishing contact with the environment. The manic-depressive retains this to a large degree, though his internal turmoil causes him to distort the feeling-quality of the world which he perceives.

This distinction might be illustrated by comparing the reactions of an excited manic patient with an excited schizophrenic. The former, for example, will respond to the door bell or the entrance of a nurse by some such remark as "Someone at the door," or a greeting to the nurse. It is a fleeting kind of interest but still an expression of response which contrasts with the lack of apparent awareness of the schizophrenic of any changes in his surroundings. He continues to express excitement in a monotonous way related entirely to his fantasies and unmodified by the activities that go on about him.

Because the schizophrenic person is no longer stimulated or inhibited by the attitudes of other people he freely acts out in ways that are ordinarily subjected to social restraint. Hostility directly and indiscriminately expressed, complete dependency, erotic behavior of the most primitive kind are part of his symptomatology.

We have observed that part of the schizophrenic syndrome expresses a renunciation and denial of the world; part of it represents restitutional attempts to replace by means of hallucinations and delusions that which is denied. His turbulent and confused desires and impulses become in this way an accepted and significant part of reality. The "voices" he hears are outward projections of thoughts he could not acknowledge as his own and which he explains as being those of authorities which try to control him. For example, a woman of fifty complained that "people in Washington" were putting thoughts into her head—obscene and violent thoughts. "I would never have had such ideas of my own." Her delusion in this way served to protect her against the breaking through of her own repressed and ego-denied impulses. A man whose intelligence quotient according to hospital tests was 145 (ranking him as "genius") sat day after day scribbling unintelligible notes, stating that he was writing a history of the world. He was able in this way to reconcile his complete dependence and social inadequacy with a sense of importance befitting one of his intellectual endowment.

Although delusions and hallucinations, like dreams, serve often for wish fulfillment, they may also like dreams reflect the person's guilt and anxiety. In so far as the schizophrenic experiences self-glorifying and gratifying concepts, he has been successful in his psychotic adjustment. He has replaced an intolerable reality with one fashioned according to his own needs. A psychotic solution, however, like a neurotic one, often fails. The sense of failure and guilt which the patient denies by projecting it outside himself still tortures him though its real meaning is unacknowledged. Terrifying ideas of persecution or of doom indicate a sense of conflict which persists despite the extremes of denial and distortion.

Schizophrenia is a malignant type of psychosis but it does not have a hopeless prognosis. Spontaneous recoveries after well-established breakdown are about 15 per cent. Some believe that this percentage can be considerably increased by early and adequate treatment. The outlook depends a good deal on the relationship between the symptoms and the previous personality. If the history is that of a gradual, insidious failure in adaptation beginning early in life, with no particularly traumatic precipitating cause, the chances of recovery are practically nil because the patient has had no experience in successful living, no once satisfactory patterns which he could refashion. This is true of the so-called simple schizophrenic. He has always been in poor rapport with reality and his breakdown represents his reactions to the progressively more difficult demands of maturity.

The most hopeful prognosis is that of the "schizophrenic episode." This is a sudden and dramatic flareup of schizophrenic symptoms at a time of great stress and strain in a person who had previously established a good social adjustment. Such episodes are frequent among men in military service, and they usually tend to clear up with supportive treatment and a change of environment. It must be remembered that lesser degrees of reality denial, projection of blame, reassuring fantasy formation are commonly utilized by all human beings and it is not surprising that these mechanisms are utilized to a pathological extent in situations of great difficulty. If they have not been interwoven into the character pattern they may be used and then discarded.

The prognosis for recovery from schizophrenic symptoms depends, therefore, not on the degree of violence or bizarre quality of the symptoms but rather on the patient's basic personality background.

In contrast to the well demarcated psychotic *episode*, a schizophrenic *process* implies a way of living manifested in the earliest attitudes. These attitudes have been described as those of the person of withdrawn or daydreaming character. They do not, of course, ordinarily culminate in a psychotic breakdown, but if the inefficiency of the behavior pattern leads to a cumulative sense of defeat and loss of interest, such a breakdown may occur.

This brings up again the question of causation. Is the schizophrenic patient the product of defective heredity—unalterably predisposed to psychosis—or is he reacting as anyone might react to an intolerably difficult series of circumstances? Or is this a disease of the brain, explicable in physiological terms?

As one observes this condition, one is impressed with the fact that the patients differ a great deal as to the relative strength of constitutional or environmental factors in the development of their psychosis. The history in some cases suggests a defective adaptive capacity from early childhood; in other cases the disordered state seems to be a logical reaction to extremely adverse circumstances. This is perhaps not too different from the situation in general medicine. Some persons are, for example, apparently more vulnerable by heredity to carcinoma or tuberculosis, yet we know that the environmental factor of irritants in the one case and massive infection in the other have much to do with the development of the disease. We might repeat that in the field of psychiatric disorder every person has his range of tolerance, and adaptive problems which would bring about the extreme disorganization of a schizophrenic psychosis in one person might cause a less extreme reaction in another. There is, however, no evidence to indicate that schizophrenia is a clearly inherited disease as is, for example, hemophilia. It is, therefore, most constructively handled by preventive attention to environmental factors which favor in the young person a progressive pattern of failure, retreat, and failure.

There have been many theories as to the significance of organic factors in schizophrenia. We know, of course, that its symptoms are not those of organic brain disease. The memory and orientation functions which we shall see later to be diagnostic of brain damage are not present here. A schizophrenic patient may, if his cooperation be won, perform well on tests for intellectual capacity. None of the neurological signs of central nervous system involvement is present, nor have the numerous autopsies of these patients revealed any specific changes—gross or microscopic—characteristic of the group.

This does not rule out the fact that there may be some less clearly defined disturbance affecting central nervous system metabolism, contributing to a greater or lesser degree to the patient's lowered capacity for adaptation. Continued research in this field is desirable, applied not only to the problem of schizophrenia but of manic-depressive and paranoid psychoses as well.

The schizophrenic process is a deeply regressive one. Perception and acknowledgment of the facts of one's environment are the earliest adaptive functions. Loss of these functions means a return to a state analogous in many ways to the self-centered state of the young infant who has not yet clearly established what is himself and what is external world. The psychotic patient superimposes on this narcissistic and dreamlike way of life a preoccupation with fragments of his past experience. He differs in this way from the infant, whose functions strain outward and forward, striving for understanding and mastery of his environment. The schizophrenic turns inward and backward, seeking perhaps the vaguely remembered Nirvana of his earliest existence but troubled by nightmares, engaged still by the need to find, though only in fantasy, the significance and acceptance he craves.

We have observed that schizophrenia is characterized by a wide diversity of symptoms, all of which may, however, be related either to the patient's denials of external reality or to his delusional and hallucinatory attempts to substitute for the denied reality. The "simple" schizophrenic process we described as largely a denial and retreat. This type of patient may at the time of his breakdown show some more florid symptoms of delusion and hallucination, but the most characteristic feature of his disturbance is the gradual renunciation of attempts at active dealing with the world. It is a negative process for the most part.

Another type of schizophrenia which expresses retreat even more dramatically is that known as catatonic stupor. The catatonic patient shows an extreme immobility and unresponsiveness, remaining in one position for hours, inactive even to the point of failing to swallow his own saliva and failing to blink his eyes in response to corneal stimulation. This stuporous condition sometimes alternates with a state of wildest excitement in which the patient acts with complete disregard of his environment. Although catatonic schizophrenia seems to represent more profound regression than the simple type of this condition, the prognosis for recovery is better. Onset is ordinarily more sudden and not so clearly an exaggeration of the basic character. A fairly good percentage of these patients recover. If, however, a catatonic episode is grafted on to a simple schizophrenic process, then the outlook for cure is unfavorable.

In some cases the delusions of the patient are his outstanding symptoms, particularly delusions of persecution and so-called ideas of reference. This group is known as the paranoid schizophrenia group. The patient is obsessed by plots against him, by secret messages sent to him over the radio, telephone, or by voices he hears. Everything about him is distorted to fit into this system. The symptoms of these patients are largely restitutional rather than reality-denying. They are most active in attempting symbolically to manipulate their situation. It might seem, therefore, that their outlook for recovery should be good. Unfortunately, paranoid ideas once formulated have a tendency to persist, for reasons which we shall examine later. The prognosis, however, depends again upon how firmly this distorted attitude has been woven into the personality structure.

The fourth type of schizophrenia, the hebephrenic, appears as an acute and stormy disorganization of function with a great many bizarre and highly symbolic symptoms which lack the better organized quality of the paranoid type. There is extreme detachment from the surroundings, much preoccupation with transitory and shifting delusions, wide swings of mood. If the condition does not clear up within a few months it often progresses rapidly into a state of so-called deterioration.

Not all schizophrenic patients deteriorate even when they do not recover. There are thousands of them who continue for their lifetimes to make simple adjustments to hospital routine or to protective and undemanding situations in their homes. The process of deterioration does not represent an actual destruction of function such as we see in organic brain disease. Rather it seems to be a progressive drawing away into a more and more unresponsive state, a vegetative and completely self-centered existence in which interest even in the restitutional fantasies seems to be lost.

Strangely enough, it has been observed that even seriously deteriorated patients can at times by patient and persistent effort be re-activated to some degree. A so-called "total push" * approach to these persons, making use of every possible encouragement and pleasant stimulus, has at times brought out responses of feeling and activity which had long been dormant.

* A. Myerson, "Total Push Method" (*Amer. Jour. Psychiatry*, January, 1940), p. 95.

Two Patients

A very brief summary and contrast of two schizophrenic patients may help to clarify some of the distinctions we have been discussing.

A sixteen-year-old son of a prominent executive was brought to the hospital because of progressive complaints of fatigue and disinterest and because he had recently made vague statements to the effect that his mother was a dangerous woman. He asserted that only he knew this and that it was up to him to protect his younger sister against her. There had been outbreaks of verbal attack on the mother and other outbreaks of great fearfulness during which the patient seemed terrified. The history is that of a boy who had always seemed, according to his mother, "cold and disinterested." He seldom if ever demonstrated affection for his family, had few friends, spent most of his time in solitary activity or playing with his young sister whom he alternately teased and protected. His school record was good but he took no part in extracurricular activities. His parents were unhappily married. The mother, deeply attached to her own mother, was a chronically depressed woman who resented her dominating husband and considered her children a burdensome responsibility. The father was a stern, ambitious, successful man who was disappointed in his shy, withdrawn son and compared him with the mother's brother, who had had a psychotic breakdown. As the boy entered adolescence he became increasingly uncommunicative and preoccupied. He seemed uneasy in the presence of girls. Gradually even his school work became less efficient, and he told his father he was having difficulty in concentration. He became irritable around home, particularly with his mother, who said, "Everything I do displeases him." Finally, after a period of insomnia and restless agitation he expressed his ideas about his mother. He said that he felt better after "discovering the truth" about her.

The other patient, a man of thirty-five, was a handsome and successful business man who had recently been promoted to a responsible position. At the same time his wife, whose relationship to him was a warmly supportive one, became pregnant and expressed much pleasure in this event which was, however, undesired by the patient. His symptoms began within a few weeks of the time he began his new work. He complained first of vague anxiety which soon took the form of a sense of being contaminated and of contaminating others around him. He insisted on going about nude, singing and orating, weeping and laughing. In the hospital he reacted violently to restrictions, expressed delusions of a megalomaniac (self-glorifying) sort, talking incessantly. This man's history is that of a "good" boy, apparently well adjusted and well liked. His father was a quiet, passive man, his mother a strong, dominating woman. A younger brother was described as more independent and aggressive than the patient, who always seemed to feel unable to compete with him. He considered this brother to be the mother's favorite, though he himself tried in every way to please her. His high school and college years were apparently successful, socially and academically. He later, however, expressed some anxiety over the fact that he had always been expected to undertake responsibilities that he really did not feel capable of handling. This was apparently because his good appearance and poised manner gave an impression of greater strength than he really possessed. The breakdown occurred at a time when his responsibilities were suddenly increased, indicating that at this point his adaptive capacities were strained beyond tolerance.

Both these patients were treated with insulin plus intensive psychotherapy. The man recovered and resumed a successful though somewhat modified career. The boy did not recover. The first history illustrates a schizophrenic process: a withdrawn, deprived, and restricted way of life which does not give adequate preparation for the expanding problems of transition into maturity. The sexual conflicts and the demands for more independent activity superimposed by the biologic state of adolescence were sufficient to disorganize the personality.

The second history is typical of a schizophrenic episode occurring in a person of relatively good previous adaptation, as a reaction to greatly increased environmental demands. As long as this person and those close to him accept his limitations he can function adequately. Treatment is directed toward developing in him an insight into his difficulties and a franker handling of them.

Treatment

Treatment of schizophrenia, once the break with reality has occurred, is obviously very difficult because of the patient's inability or unwillingness to communicate by words or feeling responses with the therapist. A sympathetic and persistent attempt over a long period to learn the meaning of the patient's language and mannerisms, thus building a bond of understanding, is occasionally of therapeutic value. Such therapy is of permanent effect, however, only if the patient's confidence and interest are sufficiently aroused so that he allows himself to take over ego attitudes of the therapist to a significant degree. Otherwise the patient merely accepts his physician into his own psychotic world, shares his fantasies with him, so to speak. The function of the therapist is to serve as a link to reality. He will be rejected as long as he remains defined entirely as representative of the alien world. He must, therefore, identify himself first with the patient, yet in this process he must retain the strength of his more realistic position or his capacity for influence is lost.

For example, one can treat a patient with a delusion of persecution only by listening sympathetically to the delusion and developing some understanding of what this idea means to the patient. Any attempt at "reasoning" in the initial contact only strengthens the patient's defense. Once the schizophrenic patient has developed trust in the therapist the latter may attempt gradually to interpret the meaning of the delusional idea and work toward a more objective attitude toward it. One may casually remark something to the effect that in view of the patient's unhappy experiences it is not surprising that he has become very sensitive on this subject and perhaps tends to exaggerate, and the like. The rapport built up in this way is a fragile thing, easily threatened by a shade too authoritative an attitude or, on the other hand, by inadequate authority. Obviously, it is successful only in the rare instances where opportunity exists for a prolonged period of treatment which can weather many vicissitudes of progress, regression, and progress.

Various forms of group therapy are of value in institutional treatment. Group discussions led by a therapist, during which the less seriously disorganized patients are encouraged to express insight, have the beneficial effect of favoring identification within a nonthreatening common group and acceptance of the leader in a kind of benign-parent role. Occupational therapy and psychodrama encourage participation and self-expression in a protected situation, overcoming some of the schizophrenic tendency to withdrawal. The "total push" idea of treatment by a profusion of pleasantly stimulating situations (music, good food, games, and the like) has had beneficial results.

The value of so-called shock treatment in schizophrenia is controversial. Reports vary from up to 80 per cent of cures in early cases reported by some to a rate of about 15 per cent (no improvement over the untreated recovery rate) by others. Patients treated early by any form of attention will of course, respond better than those who have already established a chronic psychosis. It may in time be demonstrated that a certain percentage of schizophrenic patients have a constitutional predisposition to psychosis which is related in some way to defects in physiologic functioning. In this group some form of physical-chemical therapy could presumably, by improving the efficiency of the "tools of adaptation" (the central nervous system), overcome the patient's tendency to failure and retreat. Research in this field is being carried out.

It seems obvious that the most promising therapeutic approach to the problem of schizophrenia—as indeed to that of all neuroses and psychoses—is the preventive one. We have seen these disorganizations as reactions to failure in adaptation, the origins of which often lie in early years of life. The problem of achievement of better mental hygiene as prophylaxis against the tragic toll of psychotic breakdown is a problem not for the physician alone but for concerted public effort. It will be discussed in greater detail later.

Paranoia and Paranoid States

The third type of psychosis, *paranoia*, represents an exaggeration of a pattern of human adaptation which is unfortunately very common. We have already described the paranoid character traits as representing a denial of failure by utilization of the expedient of blaming someone or something else. We recognize these character traits as the result of inability to acknowledge defeat. They occur in the person whose experience has made him suspicious and hostile. Typically he is energetic by constitution and has been conditioned to strongly competitive attitudes. If he is fairly successful in life and particularly if he is fortunate in establishing adult love relationships, his paranoid tendencies may occasion no difficulty; he is known as a strong, dominant person. If, however, he fails and failure leads to increase of his hostile, uncooperative attitude which predisposes to further failure—then the vicious circle is set up which may culminate in psychosis.

Paranoid tendencies being so common in our culture, it is not surprising that this motif colors much psychotic and neurotic ideation. We have observed it in the schizophrenic patient; often it is an outstanding symptom of this disorder. It is less frequently observed in manic-depressive psychosis, though persecutory thoughts do play a part in some depressive states. In organic brain disease paranoid ideas are often conspicuous. It would seem that in any state of severe disorganization, whether on the basis of bodily or emotional stress, the disturbed person often seeks relief by "projection."

For purposes of classification we distinguish, in addition to these paranoid components of other psychoses, two syndromes in which the essential symptoms are persecutory delusions. These are *paranoia*, sometimes known as true paranoia or paranoia vera, and a more diffuse disturbance known as *paranoid state*.

True paranoia is a relatively rare psychosis occurring usually in middle to late life, characterized by delusions of persecution in a person who is otherwise in good contact with reality. The idea is fixed and consistent, often acted on. Aside from this one delusional system the person appears "normal." Often the idea is one that could be true and if one were to grant its veracity everything which the patient says and does is logical and warranted. The patient himself may realize that his idea is considered to be delusional; hence he conceals it when it seems wise to do so. For this reason he is a difficult person to deal with. He acknowledges no need for help and is sufficiently aware of his realistic situation to avoid hospitalization; also, since his delusion is associated with strong emotion and complete conviction, he tends to be motivated by it to actions which range from letter writing and litigation to murder.

In paranoia it is as though a certain idea is dissociated from the rest of the patient's thinking. Sensation, perception, and their factual interpretations prevail in relation to everything outside this restricted area. The patient is capable of logical thinking in every respect except this. Here no amount of proof, no reasoning can shake his conviction. Within this area he is psychotic; that is, he judges reality according to his symptom instead of judging his symptom according to reality. It is similar in a way to what the conversion hysteria patient does with a bodily function. He develops, for example, a paralysis of an arm by dissociating it from control of his otherwise normally functioning nervous system. The paranoiac sets apart a certain delusional idea of persecution which cannot be touched by his otherwise normally functioning mental processes.

The delusional idea in true paranoia has a less bizarre character than it does in paranoid schizophrenia. Sometimes it may sound thoroughly plausible and the patient may win converts to his cause. A man, for example, was hospitalized because of his threats to kill his brother whom he accused of having a love affair with his (the patient's) wife. All investigations proved his accusations to be without foundation. Yet the patient's story was quite plausible. Sometimes in talks with these patients one will be able to uncover more fantastic ideas underlying the original complaint. For example, an elderly woman accused her son-in-law of plotting to kill her. Gradually as she became interested in unfolding her story she explained that the son-in-law was the reincarnation of a lover who had wronged her in her youth and who had from time to time over the years appeared in various forms to persecute her.

The delusional idea may or may not be associated with hallucinations. One woman of seventy, who called the police to report "immoral goings-on" in the neighboring apartment, led the physician outside and pointed to bushes under which she said people were "carrying on." She described in detail the appearance of the people involved. Auditory hallucinations in the form of "voices" are sometimes described as part of the system. The hallucinations of the paranoiac are not as diffuse as those of the schizophrenic.

The symptoms of true paranoia differ from those of paranoid schizophrenia not only in their generally less bizarre character but also in their clearer and more definitely circumscribed nature. They do not shift; once established they are held and reacted to consistently. In the schizophrenic these ideas are more vague and changing. They are, therefore, seldom reacted to with the violence and direct activity seen in the paranoiac.

Another differentiating point is the more adequate emotional reaction of the paranoiac. He shows strong and often violent feelings suitable to his ideas. He is angry, outraged, resentful. The paranoid schizophrenic usually gives evidence of little feeling about the persecutory ideas he verbalizes, or if he does it is in occasional outbursts, with apathy or cheerfulness between. He is less predictable than the paranoid patient. He may suddenly attack on the basis of his ideas, but this is a rare occurrence and is of an impulsive nature rather than a carefully planned procedure as it is with the paranoid patient.

Obviously both the paranoid and schizophrenic patients are potentially destructive but the former, with his good general contact and his consistently formulated idea, is more frequently able to express his resentment in homicide or other antisocial acts.

The prognosis for well-established true paranoia is believed to be hopeless for recovery. The delusional idea is the patient's final defense against a sense of intolerable defeat. He has established it so firmly beyond reach of reason or persuasion that it cannot be touched. However, this hopeless outlook does not necessarily apply to more transitory and diffuse persecutory ideas occurring at times of physical or emotional stress and strain. Even paranoid schizophrenic patients occasionally recover, and persecutory ideas in depressed states tend to clear up along with the depression.

The other psychotic manifestation of this nature is the condition known as *paranoid state*. Here it is difficult to determine where a mere character deviation leaves off and a psychosis begins. The symptoms of paranoid state are again persecutory delusions but they differ from those of true paranoia in not being clearly circumscribed. Just as a person with much free-floating anxiety may attach it now to a physical symptom and now to a phobic idea, so the paranoid patient may attach his sense of persecution to many different circumstances. He complains usually of the persons with whom he is directly associated. His history is that of inability to cooperate with his colleagues in school or at work. He has few if any friends. If he marries he is almost certain to develop pathologic jealousy of his mate, and to accuse the husband or wife of infidelity. He often feels that people talk about him or look at him in strange ways, and he may create trouble for himself by making accusations of this kind. His ideas are exaggerated but they are not as bizarre as are those of the schizophrenic, and his feelings about them are strong and consistent.

A woman of fifty, for example, who had been in and out of institutions for ten years, once threw a glass of water at a co-worker because she heard her say, "Some people are like that." At another time she approached the manager of a restaurant and complained that men at an adjoining table looked at her in a peculiar way. This woman was an intelligent, well-educated person who was able to work efficiently and was in good contact with the world about her except for her tendency constantly to find unwarranted cause for complaint against her associates.

Paranoid tendencies are widely prevalent, and there is indeed no clear-cut line here that divides the psychotic from the nonpsychotic. Ideas that would be considered delusional in one culture are accepted in another. In our Western civilization we do not make accusations of the "evil eye," as do some more primitive groups. The Western cultures do, however, attach blame in sweeping and illogical ways to persons or situations which act as scapegoats for a national sense of frustration or inadequacy. In politics and religion ideas often are expressed which are as inaccessible to reason as are the delusions of the paranoid patient. The distinctions are made on the basis of the plausibility of the idea, the number of persons believing it, and the social acceptability of the manner in which it is presented. The frustrated and ineffectual little man who complains bitterly that the Government is spying on him is locked up "because he might be dangerous." It isn't feasible, unfortunately, to incarcerate the strong and successful rabble-rouser who brings about murder and oppression of defenseless minority groups. Yet the accusations which release all this rage and aggression are for the most part as psychotic as the ravings of the paranoiac.

The paranoid person sees the world as a hostile place. His characteristic attitude toward his fellow-man is that of suspicion. The basis of his difficulty, therefore, would seem to be a sense of isolation and rejection. He feels unloved. As a substitute for happiness in close personal relationships he has tended to emphasize success and dominance, demanding in this way acceptance by the world.

The isolated attitude of this person may often be seen clearly as a product of his early life situation. In the first years of life a child judges the people about him as loving and rejecting, benign and threatening, demanding and reassuring. When the balance among these elements is weighted too heavily on the side of the negative components, the child establishes a defensive pattern of adaptation. Like the dog which has been kicked too often, he tends to regard any approach as a potentially threatening one.

The deep and intolerable sense of failure against which the persecutory delusion acts as a defense can in most cases be recognized as a failure in love. The person is unable adequately to love and be loved. He may, to be sure, have a history of other defeating circumstances leading up to the breakdown: loss of position or of money, for example. But these difficulties may often be observed as the result of his symptoms rather than the cause of them. His history, too, gives us characteristically the impression of a person to whom success in any activity was important not for itself but as a compensation for the barrenness of emotional isolation.

An element of latent homosexuality is revealed so frequently in the study of these patients as to be certainly more than a coincidence. It is ordinarily completely denied consciously and strongly protested, but it appears in dreams and fantasies and often the delusion acts as a defense against it. This has been observed particularly in ideas of infidelity which serve to "excuse" the patient for his own failure in heterosexual love and which often indicate a good deal of fantasy and emotional involvement in thought about the "seducer" of the wife or husband.

The milder, more shifting, and less well-organized paranoid states may be treated psychotherapeutically with a chance of success. Because of their suspicion, these patients are critical and demanding of the therapist; however, their need for a supportive personal relationship is so intense that they reach out for help.

The Damaged Brain

The distortions of perception and interpretation which we observe in psychotic symptoms must be looked upon as total reaction patterns rather than as specific defects. A paranoid or schizophrenic delusion or a depressed attitude can be understood only in terms of the patient's personality and in the light of his social history. We see these symptoms as attempts at adaptation under difficult circumstances, having a meaning and purpose to the patient, however far they may deviate from accepted standards of reality.

Inasmuch as every individual is a psychosomatic unit, we know that the quality of his adaptive reactions may be affected by his physiologic state as well as by his emotional and ideational levels of functioning. The psychotic syndromes which we have described have not, to be sure, been found to be related specifically to any damage to the bodily structure. It is obvious, however, that bodily integrity and particularly the integrity of the central nervous system are necessary if one is to be able to sense and perceive, comprehend and judge his life situation and to deal with it effectively.

Damage to or constitutional deficiency of the brain interferes with these capacities, creating a state of defectiveness. The psychiatric disorders which result from brain damage are easily recognized as distinct in their symptomatology from the neurotic and psychotic reactions we have described, though these reactions may be superimposed on them.

Amentia

A constitutional or early determined lack of adequate brain development results in mental deficiency or *amentia* of varying severity. Persons handicapped in this way are ordinarily not psychotic but their social adjustment is limited by their inability to comprehend facts or to retain them in memory. The learning process, therefore, proceeds haltingly. In the seriously defective idiot and imbecile groups, ability to learn even the simplest routines of self-care may be lacking.

The mentally deficient person, like any other, uses the abilities he has to deal with the situation he is in. If environmental demands are not too great he may function in a well-integrated though limited way. Such an individual is in fact less subject to the emotional conflicts associated with guilt, ambition, disillusionment, and the like. He is, however, often subjected to a great deal of frustration, and unless his environment can be adapted to his capacities he may develop behavior patterns of a socially unacceptable nature. Lacking to a large extent the capacity for symbolism, he does not tend toward the more complicated neurotic and psychotic symptoms. Rather, he is inclined toward primitive outbursts of rage and violence, suspicious and surly withdrawal, or a kind of apathetic, depressed attitude. In most cases, however, the mentally deficient person if well treated responds with behavior which is normal for one of his limitations.

There are exceptions to this principle in cases of amentia where the brain damage is such as to cause pathologic stimulation of certain areas of the brain or to allow relative overactivity of some areas. In such cases the patient may show deviations of behavior which seem to have no relationship to emotional conflict or the environmental situation. Outbreaks of extreme excitement, violence, and anger are sometimes observed in brain-damaged children and adults even under the best of care.

We might, therefore, consider the symptoms of the mentally deficient person as of three categories. First there are the intellectual deficiencies which interfere with learning and keep him more or less incapable of an independent, self-supporting existence. These deficies can be measured by tests of intelligence. Second, there are his reactions to his life situation. These may be normal (for him) or they may express his frustrations in poorly adaptive behavior. Third, there are in some cases symptoms meaningless as personality reactions; they are direct results of destructive or irritative processes in the brain.

Congenital mental defect is in most cases incurable. One outstanding exception to this is *cretinism*, which is a state of thyroid underactivity having amentia as one of its symptoms. Children in whom this diagnosis can be made respond dramatically to continued treatments by thyroid extracts. Treatment must be begun early if permanent physical and mental damage is to be avoided.

Another congenital disorder sometimes confused with cretinism is *Mongolism*; so-called because of the patient's facial appearance. The cause of this condition is unknown and no hereditary basis for it has been established. It is characterized by cardiac and skeletal abnormalities, a slant-eyed facies (face and aspect), and severe mental retardation. Mongoloid children usually do not develop serious behavior problems, being rather cheerful and docile as a general thing. They seldom live to maturity and are not able to be self-supporting, though they can learn simple routines.

Aside from these specific types of developmental defect, we can observe cases of amentia which are related to underdevelopment of the brain or to the accumulation of excessive fluid around it. In some instances there is no external appearance of structural defect. Injury at birth may result in mental retardation, though this is probably a rare occurrence. Even such severe birth injuries as result in the spastic child do not ordinarily damage this child's mental capacity. Other early-acquired damage may be the result of infection (particularly encephalitis or brain syphillis) or of direct injury.

Delirium and Dementia

Damage to the brain which takes place after normal development has been accomplished results in *delirium,* if the injury is acute, or in *dementia* if it is chronic.

The causes of delirium or dementia are numerous and varied including, of course, any form of injury imposed from without as well as any disorganizations of internal functioning which directly or indirectly affect the brain. The symptoms are not in most cases specifically related to the cause. A person with, for example, a toxic delirium resulting from drug poisoning may react in the same way as one with a severe infection, or another with a fractured skull. Similarly, dementias on the basis of arteriosclerosis, syphilis, or alcoholism may manifest the same basic symptoms of defect. To these are added, however, reactions characteristic of the person involved which tend to bring out similar features in the separate groups, as we shall see later.

Delirium is a medical problem and treatment is directed toward overcoming the pathologic state which has produced it. In addition, it is important to give consideration to the fact that a delirious episode may be a very disturbing experience to the patient involved, so that as he recovers he may develop a good deal of secondary anxiety. If his physician treats this with reassurance and frankness, and if the patient does not retain permanent brain damage, he ordinarily recovers completely.

A condition known as *toxic-exhaustive psychosis* combines the features of delirium with those of a psychosis in a way which sometimes makes it difficult to determine the primary cause. The patient has varying symptoms of physiologic disorder such as, for example, anemia, low blood pressure, loss of weight, weakness, sometimes evidences of an infectious process; in addition he manifests depressive, schizophrenic, or paranoid symptoms. The condition could be basically one of disturbed physical function interfering with adaptive efficiency, or it could be basically an adaptive failure with secondary poor nutrition predisposing to physiologic symptoms. Obviously treatment must be directed toward the total problem.

Dementia is a chronic state of mental defect, resulting directly from damage to the brain. It is a condition of loss of capacity rather than a dynamic process of maladjustment such as we see in neurosis and psychosis. The symptoms of dementia are sometimes designated as *the organic triad*. They are: impairment of memory, impairment of judgment, and disorientation in space and time. Not all these symptoms need be present in any patient but at least one of them must be if a diagnosis of dementia is to be made.

A person handicapped by dementia need not be psychotic. We recognize this fact as we observe our population of aged individuals, most of whom adjust to and with their defects of mental capacity without developing a psychosis. There seems, in fact, to be poor correlation between the degree of dementia and the severity of psychosis in those cases where psychosis does appear. For example, a patient with only a slight impairment of memory may express violent paranoid delusions whereas another individual with extreme defects of memory and orientation may be only mildly depressed.

A process of brain destruction creates serious interference with normal adaptive processes. Memory impairment narrows one's area of functioning; disorientation as to time and place favors a sense of insecurity; impaired judgment results in embarrassed or defensive attitudes. It is, therefore, not surprising that patients experiencing these frustrations will often react in one or another of the patterns of defeat we have been describing. They may show an alteration of character, becoming perhaps more withdrawn or more belligerent. They may utilize some such neurotic mechanisms as compulsive or psychopathic attitudes, or they may superimpose on their dementia a full-blown psychosis.

Although the causes of dementia comprise all conditions which could injure the brain, nevertheless there are only a few common causes. These are senility and/or arteriosclerosis, alcoholism, and central nervous system syphilis. Illinois State Hospital statistics for 1940 indicate the proportion of first admissions as: cerebral arteriosclerosis 22.6 per cent, neurosyphilis 11.3 per cent, alcoholism 10 per cent, senility 9.4 per cent. Inasmuch as most of these patients do not recover they constitute a large part of the population of our state hospitals. With better specific treatment of syphilis, dementia on this basis is steadily declining. The incidence of the degenerative processes of old age, on the other hand, is increasing as the life span is lengthened.

Thousands of old people with mild degrees of dementia are put into public institutions even though they might function much more satisfactorily on the outside. There is no other place for them; no one is willing or able to assume responsibility for their care.

This sad state of affairs is partly due to a relatively intolerant attitude in our culture toward the older generations. In part also it is because many people adapt poorly to the aging process, developing character traits which make them objectionable.

The general tendency toward intolerance of old age is perhaps a product of the Western emphasis on strength and active accomplishment, of progress to new and adventurous ways of living. The wisdom of experience is disregarded in favor of the audacity of youth. This restless and forward-striving attitude makes the role of the aging ancestor a relatively unimportant one. Then, too, because the life span has increased so rapidly in recent generations there is actually no adequate provision in most communities for suitable care of men and women disabled by old age.

The person limited in his activities by senile-arteriosclerotic dementia functions best if he can feel useful within his capacity. The right balance of protection and encouragement on the part of his children or others around him allows a relatively harmonious adaptation.

We have observed, however, that the situation is complicated further by the attitudes and behavior of the person himself. Adaptation to the disabilities of a dementing process depends on the kind of character patterns already established. A good resolution of the problems of the aged or otherwise disabled depends in final analysis, therefore, on a way of living which has its foundations in early childhood. From this point of view we might say that treatment of the dementias and psychoses of later life begins with the treatment of children. The child who loves and respects his parents will give them consideration as they grow old, and the aged person who has been given loving consideration as a child will be less likely to create, by his behavior patterns, serious problems for his children.

PART III

The Problem of Treatment

chapter 10

AGENCIES OF HEALTH

> Humane treatment may raise up one in whom the divine image has long been obscured.
> —Fyodor Dostoyevsky: *The House of the Dead*

As we survey the wide scope of psychiatric disorders, which manifest themselves in varying degrees of character distortion and in physical illness as well as more specifically in neurosis and psychosis, we are impressed with the complicated nature of the treatment problem. If we grant—as it seems we must—the psychiatric nature of such diverse difficulties as, for example, enuresis and food resistance in children, stammering, withdrawn, paranoid, or depressive personality traits, alcoholism, homosexuality (overt or latent), much criminality, and approximately 50 per cent of medical symptoms presented to the general physician, we realize that our relatively very small group of trained psychiatrists * can deal with only a small percentage of the people who could use their help. Also, these medical specialists

---

* There were in 1953 between seven and eight thousand members of the American Psychiatric Association and about 500 members of the American Psychoanalytic Association.

The psychiatrist is a physician who after completing his medical training has spent several years in psychiatric studies, after which he has passed a series of examinations in his specialty given by the American Board of Psychiatry and Neurology. This procedure of training is the same as that followed by any other medical specialists, such as, for example, the dermatologists or pediatricians. If the psychiatrist plans to practice psycho-

are for the most part grouped in the large cities, hence unavailable to much of our population. When treatment is available it must often be intensive and prolonged, and as a consequence too expensive for those of closely limited finances.

Even when these difficulties do not exist, psychiatric treatment is not sought in many situations where it would be most effective because the need for it is unrecognized or unacknowledged as a result of prejudicial attitudes. For example, acute anxiety states may be treated as medical problems for years because the physician either fails to recognize the condition or feels he would antagonize his patient by suggesting psychiatric referral. Early character disorders in children are too often ignored and even an early psychotic condition may be denied frank recognition by the patient, his family, and even sometimes his doctor, until it has reached full-blown development.

These evasive attitudes are the result of the sense of shame and mystery which still surrounds so-called mental disorder. It is socially acceptable to have a diagnosis of appendicitis but if the doctor tells the patient that his abdominal distress is the expression of emotional disturbance this has about it an air of moral condemnation. "You mean it's all in my head!" or even, "Do you mean to sug-

---

analysis, he applies also for admission to an institute for training in psychoanalysis (there are thirteen such institutes in this country). His work there is usually correlated with his other graduate work in psychiatry so that he is preparing for his specialty examinations and meeting psychoanalytic training requirements at the same time. As an important part of his psychoanalytic training, he must himself be psychoanalyzed, after which he must analyze several patients under close supervision of an Institute staff member. In most medical schools the tendency is more and more toward integrating this specific training into the university programs and in time it will no doubt be a part of the regular curriculum in postgraduate psychiatry, though with some modifications in the rigidity and exclusiveness of its teachings.

gest I'm crazy?" might be the response, and the physician does not always have a clear enough understanding of the condition to be able to explain satisfactorily the fact that the condition is neither imagination nor craziness, yet clearly the result of emotional disequilibrium.

The answer to this problem is not necessarily, at least not exclusively, the training and better distribution of more psychiatrists. It seems that especial efforts should be made, first in the direction of general education, and second in the direction of better psychiatric training of those persons other than psychiatrists in position to recognize and deal with psychiatric problems.

Better Parenthood

The first means a program of mental hygiene directed particularly toward parents. A great deal of progress has already been made in this direction, largely because doctors who treat children are becoming increasingly aware of the effects of the child's life situation on his physical functioning. It has already been observed that the newer ideas about feeding and toilet training stress permissiveness and allowance for the child's attitudes rather than merely convenient routine. Then too the parents themselves absorb some awareness of the existence of psychological problems from books and articles they read and lectures they hear, so that they on the whole give a more interested and encouraging response to the psychologically minded doctor than they might have done fifty years ago.

Good rules of child care are important in the prevention of problems which interfere with satisfactory personality development. Rules alone, however, will not create the happy, cooperative family life in which the young human being thrives. Parents with serious emotional problems of their own contribute to the development of such problems in their children. It is ineffectual, therefore, to consider a child's psychiatric problem apart from those of his parents. The pediatrician may diagnose the youngster's complaint as indicative of anxieties which can be alleviated only by treatment of the mother or father. This poses a therapeutic dilemma in that the doctor has neither the time nor the training to tackle the parents' problems, nor does he feel they would respond well to his suggestions for doing so.

In communities where a child guidance clinic is available this provides a good approach to the psychiatric disorders of childhood. Such a clinic utilizes the efforts of the medical doctor, the social service worker, the psychologist, and the psychiatrist in making a diagnosis and in working out treatment plans for the child and, if indicated, for his parents. These clinics exist in several of the larger cities, and in some states have affiliated traveling clinics which visit the outlying communities. They can serve, however, to care for only a small fraction of the need. More of these clinics should be—and are being—established.

Another possibility is that of an expansion of mental hygiene projects in the schools by means of lectures and group discussions with parents, and individual conferences when requested. Such programs to be successful must meet with understanding and cooperation on the part of the teaching staff, a group which for the most part has not had adequate training in this field.

PSYCHIATRY IN GENERAL MEDICINE

This brings us to the second objective: that of better education for professional groups which could supplement or substitute for the work of the psychiatrist. Here again, a good deal of progress has been made in the past fifty years. As the functions of the psychiatrist have widened they have become interwoven more closely both with other departments of medicine and with various professional groups dealing with social problems.

A little over a hundred years ago, when the American Psychiatric Association was founded, it was known as the Association of Hospital Superintendents. Its members were the medical staffs of the state mental hospitals, physicians whose activities were concerned with administration of these institutions and care of the psychotic patients. Although many of these pioneers in the field made significant contributions in research and treatment, they were regarded by the other members of the medical profession as being a group apart, suspected of inadequacy or "queerness" because of their choice of specialty. There was little if any common interest or endeavor between psychiatrist and general physician.

The family physician of that time would have been quick to deny any awareness of psychiatric problems in his practice, yet as a matter of fact he undoubtedly practiced, for better or worse, a good deal of psychotherapy. Having an intimate knowledge of his community and of the families with which he worked, he had a background for better understanding of his patient's emotional state than does the physician of today. The situation, therefore, was one in which the psychiatrist was restricted both in his study and his practice to the problems of psychosis; whereas the general physician handled in an intuitive kind of way the lesser degrees of personality disturbance which presented themselves in the course of his practice. If the family doctor's intuitions were good this may not have worked out too badly, but it was a hit-or-miss matter.

With progress toward a more exact and technical medical education, the tendency was toward specialization and toward glorification of precise laboratory methods of treating illness. The patient thus became so divided into specialties and so impersonally regarded that his individuality was often lost sight of. Under these circumstances personality problems are dismissed as of little interest. This trend toward exact and impersonal methods in medicine reached its peak a decade or two ago and the swing now seems toward greater recognition of the patient as a whole.

Meanwhile the psychiatrist has gradually come out of isolation as he has become convinced of the fact that there is no sharp line of distinction that marks off his patients from other people. The result is that the paths of the psychiatrist and of other physicians converge and there is mutual interest in the interrelationships of physical and psychic levels of functioning manifested in most illnesses.

This shifting in attitude is reflected in the greatly increased emphasis on psychiatry in the medical curriculum. As recently as twenty-five years ago courses in this subject in most schools were limited to one descriptive of the psychoses, plus a few hours of very superficial work with neurotic patients in the clinic. At present most of the larger medical schools begin the teaching of psychiatry in the freshman year and assign a good many hours each year to the subject. Especially favorable is the tendency to present psychiatric principles not as specialized knowledge but as part of the approach to all illness. The emotional life of the child becomes part of pediatrics; medical and surgical problems are evaluated not only as involving pathology on a physiologic level but also from the standpoint of the patient's personality. Much still remains to be done, but the aim is an attitude which regards psychiatry as an integral aspect of the approach to any patient. Its importance varies, to be sure, and in some conditions is minimal, but the trend is away from sharp distinctions between medical problems and psychiatric problems.*

This tendency to apply psychiatric understanding to the problems of general medicine will have the result more and more of preparing the general physician to recognize and deal wisely with innumerable problems which are primarily the result of emotional rather than physiologic disturbance in his patients. In many cases he is the person best suited for dealing with these problems. His patients have faith in him and will turn to him readily for help, whereas they would hesitate to grant the existence of a difficulty severe enough to take to a psychiatrist. The possibilities and limitations of psychiatric treatment by the general physician will be discussed in detail later. First we should consider briefly the possibilities of other professional groups for contributing to good mental health.

* The inter-relationships may be grouped somewhat as follows:

1. The organic disorders resulting primarily from physical-chemical pathology. These include, for the most part, the infectious and neoplastic diseases and some of the traumatic, metabolic, and degenerative processes.

2. The psychiatric disorders based on organic cerebral damage: the organic psychoses.

3. The illnesses representing interaction of psychic and somatic levels of functioning: such conditions as the allergies, vascular and endocrine imbalanced states, peptic ulcer, spastic colon, many gynecologic and dermatologic disorders. Manic-depressive and schizophrenic psychosis probably belong here.

4. Functional disturbances of organs without structural pathology, representing directly an unsatisfied emotional state. These are the organ neuroses manifested in cardiac, gastrointestinal, or other vegetative symptoms as well as in excessive fatigue.

5. The conversion states in which the organ is used to symbolize a conflictual idea: conversion hysteria in its many forms.

6. Behavioral disorders without important relationship to physiologic function: paranoid, psychopathic, phobic, and obsessional states.†

† B. C. Bosselman, *Neurosis and Psychosis* (Charles C Thomas, Publisher, Springfield, Illinois, 1950).

The Psychologist's Role

The psychologists constitute a group whose training qualifies them for diagnosis and treatment in this field. Traditionally their education has been academic and theoretical. However, in recent years much more emphasis has been placed on practical application of theoretical knowledge of mental mechanisms.

Psychological tests have been formulated as guides toward better use of the individual's resources. The psychometric tests give an objective picture of learning ability, specific aptitudes or deficiencies, vocational talents. They provide information about learning and performance capacities according to our established norms. Another group of tests, characterized as projective, contribute to a deeper, more qualitative understanding of personality structure. The psychologist is able, by an analysis of the nature of responses made to standardized stimuli, to recognize problems of thinking and feeling which may not superficially be apparent.

Not only in a testing and advisory capacity but also in a directly therapeutic role the psychologist is finding an increasingly useful place in our educational institutions. In the public schools he is concerned with the child's learning abilities, with evaluation and treatment of such specific handicaps as those of speech and reading. In addition he is often the person best qualified to recognize the socially maladjusted child and to confer with parents and teacher about the problems involved. In the more progressive high schools and in most colleges the departments of psychology are utilized for advice as to the student's curriculum and vocational plans. Members of the department also contribute to the student counseling program. Here the psychologist may function independently or, when the situation warrants it, may arrange referral to a psychiatrist.

We have already mentioned the work of child guidance clinics where a collaborative approach by psychiatrist, psychologist, and psychiatric social worker has proved most effective. In this group the psychologist's first concern is diagnosis, but he participates also to a greater or less degree in treatment.

Psychological problems in industry have to do with harmonious and efficient work adaptation. Aptitude tests help to place the individual in positions for which he is well suited. Conferences of employees with the industrial psychologist bring out dissatisfactions or personal anxieties which may underlie poor performance. The psychologist serves as an intermediary between employee and employer, interpreting each to the other and contributing in this way to a more friendly atmosphere. Personality studies in industry have revealed some facts of practical importance. It is found, for example, that some employees have much greater predisposition to accidents than the average. They are accident-prone, and should therefore be employed in the less hazardous positions. Psychological studies help to determine such qualities as capacity for leadership, tact, endurance, efficiency in crisis, and the like, all of which serve as guides to satisfactory placement.

We have stressed the unfortunate consequences of the impersonal nature of modern work situations, which give the employee little sense of significance or interest. The industrial psychologist recognizes the individual and his needs and encourages him to feel a greater sense of participation in the unit.

The work of the psychologist in the armed services contributes toward more adequate selection and placement of men. During the last war much research was concerned with the formulation of tests to determine the qualities which predispose to good or to poor adjustment to military life. The Veterans Administration has utilized a large staff of psychologists for vocational rehabilitation and psychotherapeutic work with veterans. Here again collaborative efforts of all the professions involved contribute to a high degree of success in physical and mental rehabilitation.

Other institutions which utilize psychological studies are the psychiatric hospitals and the prisons. Here the objective and projective tests help to analyze the personality factors which contribute to mental breakdown and which are correlated with criminality. This knowledge is conducive to better understanding of personality deviations as cause and effect phenomena.

It is obvious that the psychologist plays a significant part in the study and treatment of problems of human adaptation. His multiple activities are of relatively recent origin and are only gradually being integrated with the functions of the psychiatrist and of the general physician.

Psychiatric Social Work

To this trio we can add another professional group which is making a very significant therapeutic contribution. This is the psychiatric social work group. Here we have personnel trained both in sociology and psychology whose interest is psychiatric problems as they are interwoven with the social structure. The worker is concerned not so much with the patient's mental mechanisms as he is with his family and group relationships and the effect which these relationships have upon his functioning.

The psychiatrically trained social worker is a relatively recent development. University courses in social service administration provide first a groundwork in sociologic and administrative principles and the practical aspects of interpersonal relationships. Then for the worker who specializes in psychiatry there are added courses in this department and experience in clinical work with psychiatric problems. The product is a professional person with a good deal of understanding of emotional problems and with contacts which make him particularly effective for evaluating the situational elements involved. He is thus capable not only of direct therapy with the disturbed person but also of bringing about necessary changes in the life situation. He can be in close touch with the family, the school, church and recreational groups; he can be of help in finding suitable occupation and in recommending legal or medical advice where it is needed. Psychiatric social workers have established good cooperative relationships with psychiatrists and in the larger communities the two groups work together well. The worker carries out much of the practical aspect of therapy and in addition is able to treat many of the simpler problems directly, thus providing treatment for many who would otherwise have no opportunity for benefiting from it. At present the need for psychiatrically trained social workers greatly exceeds the supply.

We see, therefore, a definite movement toward increasing the availability of treatment for problems of mental health. Emphasis on this is evident in the medical curricula and in the training of psychologists and social workers.

There are in addition other professional groups which have up to now no well-formulated training in psychotherapeutic principles. Particularly this applies to school teachers and pastors—both large and influential groups whose work brings them into daily contact with problems involving personality.

The Teacher and the Disturbed Child

The teacher who observes his pupils closely over periods of a year or more would seem to be in a favorable position for detecting in the young child those patterns of maladjustment which often later develop into serious personality handicaps. He knows that some children are shy and timid, withdrawn from the group; others are defensive and belligerent, suspicious of everyone. He contrasts the good-natured exuberance of the majority with the apparent unhappiness or self-absorption of others. In some cases he may even recognize the reasons for maladjustment in unfavorable parental relationships or in circumstances which in some way set the child apart. Yet with all this psychopathology constantly before them, most teachers take little or no active part in helping the child to deal with his personal problems.

There are two reasons for this failure to utilize a golden opportunity for early treatment of psychiatric difficulty. One is that the school system itself is (except for rare instances) not set up in such a way as to favor a confidential personal relationship between pupil and teacher. The other reason is the teacher's relative lack of training in psychologic principles or in therapeutic techniques.

The first difficulty results from the heavy load which the teacher must carry, and it is reinforced by certain attitudes concerning his role which favor a formal, impersonal kind of schoolroom routine. A man or woman called on to handle classes of twenty-five to forty pupils in rapid succession during each day has little leisure or energy for the problems of the individual child. The course of study is inflexible; certain facts must be uniformly learned and examinations passed, papers must be graded and, above all, order must be maintained. This latter circumstance alone absorbs a great deal of the teacher's time. He is judged according to his ability to "keep discipline." He tends, therefore, to prize the quiet, conforming members of his classes, some of whom may actually be more poorly adjusted than their noisy, rebellious classmates. Even the children themselves reflect the concept of school as a jail, teacher as a jailer. A kind of "cops and robbers" spirit prevails, according to which the child is smart if he can "put it over" on teacher who in turn is smart if he is able to control his group. This prevalent atmosphere of artificially engendered hostility is exhausting and depressing to sensitive teachers. Those who remain in spite of it often erect a kind of self-protective barrier between themselves and their pupils, emphasizing efficiency and order rather than warmth and understanding in the teacher-pupil relationships.

The deficiencies of pedagogic training in child psychology have been extreme in the past but are being more or less overcome in the present-day curricula in education. The enrichment of courses in child development, educational psychology, and the like reflects here as elsewhere the modern greater emphasis on the emotional aspects of living. As yet, however, the courses are too formal and theoretical in their presentation. The instructors have for the most part little or no experience in actually dealing with children's problems so they tend to present the material in an abstract, impersonal way, and the young teacher starting out with a demanding group of flesh-and-blood youngsters finds difficulty in applying the principles he has learned to the actual situation in which he is involved. Usually he has been given no help at all with the problems of technique. What should he do with the defensive child or with the daydreamer? What moves can be made to inspire confidence on the part of the child and his parents? How far can he go in encouraging the child to unburden his anxieties without thereby arousing the child's greater anxieties and guilts for having dared to unburden himself? Is it possible to win the parent as an ally in solving the pupil's problems and at the same time make the parent aware of the contribution of his own defects to the boy's or girl's difficulty? These are dilemmas that challenge even the highly trained child psychiatrists; it is not surprising that most teachers turn away from any approach to them.

It would seem that teacher training programs should move in the direction of the clinical method. This is the trend in medical schools: stress on actual contact of student with patient and application of theoretical principles as they are learned. A diagnosis is more meaningful as the student sees it in a person rather than in a book, and treatment of the condition diagnosed attains sureness as it is carried out in an actual situation. This procedure applied to pedagogy would mean greater emphasis on practice teaching and on interviews with children, preferably also some instruction and perhaps some experience in dealing with parents.

The teacher, however well trained, could not of course expect to spend much if any time in actual treatment of personality difficulties. His role should be that of recognizing the difficulties and of establishing a cooperative relationship with child and parent which would make a therapeutic approach possible. He should be familiar with the resources in his community for medical, psychiatric, and social service referral. In rare instances, however, it has always been possible for a teacher with good insight and warm human interest to accomplish a great deal directly with a confused and unhappy child. Many adults look back with gratitude to some one teacher whose guidance and understanding was of incalculable benefit to him in his childhood. Unfortunately, these instances appear to be greatly outnumbered by those of damage done to boys and girls by rigid, hostile teachers operating without concern for the feelings and capacities of their pupils.

Psychiatry and Religion

The role of the pastor in psychotherapy brings up the question of the interrelationships of psychiatry and religion.

The ends to be achieved by religion and by psychiatry are in many ways identical. Both strive for a satisfactory sublimation of man's basic drives for direct gratification into a socially constructive pattern of living. Both realize that this accomplishment depends on a large component of interest in and consideration for one's fellow-man. In our discussions of the problems of adaptation we have emphasized the need to give up the self-centeredness of early childhood and to establish personal relationships in which the component of love overbalances hate; we have observed that true maturity is measured in terms of ability to give freely to others. The neurotic and psychotic syndromes which we have examined are indications of failure to establish a constructive, out-going pattern of life. The patient is in most cases beset by hate and distrust of other people, torn by the conflicts between these negative feelings and his ideas of what his feelings should be. In the church as in the psychiatrist's office he is encouraged to work toward friendly, cooperative relationships with the world about him.

The methods of achieving good adaptation by substitution of love for hate, construction for destruction, faith for doubt are, however, quite different in religion from the methods of psychiatry. In general, religion emphasizes increased repression whereas psychiatry emphasizes recognition of the repressed and realistic handling of it according to the needs of the situation. The church says, "Love your enemies," a law which up to now human nature has not been able to assimilate. Psychiatry in a less direct way works toward the better self-understanding which allows a relaxation of the suspicion and exaggerated competitiveness destructive to human relationships. The one would overlay bitter and hostile attitudes with a façade of kindness and charity; and other would attempt through expression and analysis of these negative attitudes to remove much of their potency.

Certainly these techniques can learn from each other. Psychotherapy carried on in a cold and formal way with stress on the need for direct self-expression rather than for constructive social integration becomes often a barren procedure. The feeling of faith in the good which is God and of need for social rather than exclusively individual welfare as motivation for behavior are religious assets which might well be utilized in every therapeutic relationship. On the other hand, religious techniques which depend on blind acceptance of creed and which strive to overcome strong forces of hate by simply denying them are in need of some of the flexibility and tolerance of the psychiatric approach.

The nature of therapeutic pastoral counseling depends, of course, on the individual pastor and on the limitations imposed by his denomination. Diversity of creeds prevents standardized procedure but the common interest of them all is encouragement in social righteousness and identification with God's will as interpreted by their religious leaders. Christ said, "As ye would that men should do to you, do ye also to them likewise"; Confucius said, "Do not do unto others what you would not have done to yourself." These rules for living will probably never be improved upon.

Religion can contribute to better mental health both as a mystical supportive force and as a code of ethics. The Protestant Christian churches, aware of their potentialities in this respect, have in recent years devoted a good deal of study to the subject of pastoral counseling, defining its aims and limitations and working toward cooperation with other agencies which have a similar aim. Likewise, a good deal of emphasis on this problem is found in Jewish religious groups which in many instances are actively cooperating with social agencies for prophylaxis and treatment of emotional maladjustment. The Catholic priest has for generations offered consolation and renewed strength to the confessant, providing him not only with an opportunity for verbalization of his guilt but also providing peace through reconciliation with God.

Many emotionally upset people would benefit by identification with a religious group but are unable to accept any such affiliation. Sometimes their rejection is the result of disappointing, disillusioning experiences with such groups; at other times it has grown out of their distrust of parental authority which produces a generally skeptical attitude.

The therapist treating such persons should recognize their needs, should help them to understand their resistances and if possible direct them toward the kind of religious experience which they can accept. This necessitates in the therapist great objectivity and freedom from personal bias—an interest directed to the patient and his problem uninfluenced by the therapist's own attitudes. Obviously no psychiatrist can accept for himself the religious orientations of all his patients any more than he can all their political or philosophical beliefs. He should, however, be able to identify sufficiently to grasp the meaning of these experiences for the patient and evaluate them according to their constructive or destructive effect. Some patients may be using a narrow, rigid creed in a restrictive and hostile way. Treatment which makes them less defensive will relax the rigidities of their beliefs. Others may, as has been implied, be able to accept a supportive religious experience only after they have become aware of the significance of their denials of it.

The beginnings of better cooperation among churches, social service groups, and psychiatrists is evident especially in our more progressive urban centers. Mutual tolerance and understanding here provide a most desirable situation for contributing to the best possible use of all community resources "for each according to his need."

Psychotherapy

We turn now more specifically to the techniques of psychiatric treatment. The aims are common to all schools of therapy, but techniques differ widely. Always the purpose is to alleviate difficulties which manifest themselves in a patient's neurotic or psychotic symptoms. The ways by which this is attempted include medical care where this is indicated and psychotherapy in its various aspects, which range from simple support to the intensive and well-standardized techniques of psychoanalysis. The important element in every case, however, is the personal relationship established between patient and therapist. The influence of this relationship constitutes psychotherapy.

A person with a psychiatric problem usually goes first for help to his physician. In the larger and more sophisticated communities he may recognize the nature of his difficulty and go directly to the physician who specializes in psychiatry: the psychiatrist. In more limited instances, especially in universities or in some industries, he may approach the psychologist, or if the problem is one involving personal-ethical relationships he may take it to his pastor. The patient, of course, does not always realize that he has psychiatric difficulties, or he may be consciously evading this realization. In such cases the nature of the trouble may first be recognized in the course of routine medical care.

Treatment by the Physician

The general physician carries, therefore, a heavy part of the responsibility for prevention and treatment of psychiatric disorders. His preparation for this task has until recently been most inadequate. Even now his training for the recognition and handling of neurotic and psychotic disorders is by no means in proportion to the demands which these problems make within his practice.

We have already observed that there are many patients with disorders primarily emotional whom the family doctor must treat because specialized psychiatric help is not available for them. There are many others for whom referral could be arranged but who nevertheless should be treated by the general physician for various reasons. These may include children with developmental difficulties which the doctor will observe as problems of eating and elimination, or such deviations of behavior as excessive fearfulness or irritability. The symptoms are often not obvious to parents, who would be frightened and antagonized by suggestions of psychiatric care. A friendly and astute pediatrician who has the trust of the family possesses an opportunity for diagnosis and a constructive approach to those problems which involve the early dynamic aspects of interpersonal relationships. It is important that every doctor who treats children should be aware of the adaptive problems of each developmental period and be sensitive to symptoms in his young patients which indicate blocking in the normal processes of maturation. Wherever such blocking is not the result of physical or mental defect, it indicates an unsureness or uncooperativeness on the part of the child toward the world about him. He indicates this by clinging to the established patterns of infancy, or he may regress toward earlier behavior when experience becomes in some way painful for him. His parents then bring to the doctor such complaints as bedwetting, retardation in speaking or walking, feeding problems. They may also have observed in their child such unfavorable character traits as excessive timidity or fretfulness, violent temper outbursts. They may report insomnia and night terrors, unwillingness to go to bed, fear of the dark. The child's speech may be disturbed by stammering or lisping or he may develop muscular twitches (tics). Symptoms of this kind cannot be explained on an organic medical basis, yet they are often serious disturbances to the immediate well-being of the child and indicate hazards for his future.

Other psychiatric problems with which the general physician must continually deal are those expressed in somatic symptoms. We have described them as somatic neuroses or psychosomatic disorders, and have emphasized the fact that they make up a large part of every doctor's practice. He cannot escape them and he will be most successful if he accepts the problem and applies to it the same careful and objective attention which he gives to the more specifically organic diseases of his patients.

There are certain principles of psychiatric treatment that apply in every case, whoever the therapist may be. Sincerity and objectivity are particularly important. Too often the tendency of the physician is to evade the real issues of his neurotic patients, to deny or ignore them, or to belittle them as unworthy of attention. As a result, whatever he does lacks sincerity. It is not a product of interest and judgment but merely a device to placate the patient. A lack of objectivity is equally unfortunate. It favors a kind of involvement of the doctor in the patient's emotional state. This usually takes the form of an irritated, impatient reaction but it may go in the direction of too indiscriminating "sympathy" by which the therapist accepts the neurotic attitudes to such an extent as to be unable to guide the patient away from them.

The skillful physician begins his treatment of every patient with a careful examination and a history of the illness. This approach should not be less thorough for the neurotic patient, even though the diagnosis seems obvious. A person may be emotionally disturbed and yet have at the same time an organic disease which may or may not be related to his emotional state. One does not rule out the other, and it is important for winning the patient's confidence to impress him with the completeness of the examination. Otherwise he may cling to the idea of physical illness and resist a more "psychological" diagnosis. A thorough history includes not only a record of symptoms but also an impression of the person: his background, his character traits, and particularly any facts about his experience which might relate to the onset and course of his illness. If the physician concentrates exclusively on the impersonal aspects of the history he will often miss the most important diagnostic points.

After the physician has assessed the facts presented by his examination and history he must interpret these facts to the patient and it is at this point that he often fails to carry through. He is either unconvinced or is unwilling to tell his patient that the disorder expressed in the symptoms is essentially an emotional one understandable only in terms of the patient's life situation and his relationships with other people.

It is true that some persons would react with anxiety to such a diagnosis, and it must be presented to them tactfully; a few would reject it however it is presented. The latter reaction is seen particularly in the chronically hypochondriacal men or women who have long ago turned away from any attempt at frank appraisal of their symptoms and have accepted them for whatever they can get out of them. This attitude was illustrated by the remarks of a woman seen in the medical ward of a hospital. She had over the years undergone numerous surgical operations which had afforded her no relief and she talked volubly of her "adhesions." She said she and her husband had made a wager. "He bet me a hundred dollars the doctors wouldn't find anything wrong with me!"

In the great majority of cases, however, patients will accept a physician's explanation that their symptoms are the expression of a disturbed functioning of the organ involved rather than of structural damage of the organ. "Your heart is not diseased, but its function is disturbed," might be the formulation, after which the physician goes on to explain the physiologic ways by which emotion is expressed.

At this point a good deal of reassurance is often helpful, particularly to the patient with severe anxiety symptoms. Often he has reinforced the neurotic anxiety by superimposed fears of severe illness, death, or psychosis. This creates a sense of hopeless panic which intensifies his functional disorganization. He must be made to understand that he is not going to die or "go crazy" and that his symptoms are the logical result of emotional conflicts which in time he can learn to understand and to master.

Many patients with early neurotic conditions will respond very favorably to the physician who in this way expresses a sense of understanding and self-confidence. They have been frightened by the mysterious nature of their symptoms and are relieved to find that the doctor recognizes them as cause-and-effect phenomena of not uncommon occurrence and not malignant.*

So much for the physician's initial approach to the problem. The therapeutic procedures which follow must either consciously or intuitively be related to our basic concept of psychiatric symptoms as expression of breakdown in the integrative function of the ego. The equilibrium of repression has been interfered with, either by increase in strength of the repressed forces or by weakening of those which repress. We have recognized that there may be contributions to this situation from many sources. Physical as well as psychological impairments of ego-strength may be important. Fatigue, infection, anemia, inadequate diet, are possible contributing factors which the medical man is well qualified to assess. He needs in addition to cultivate an awareness of those less tangible impacts on the ego made by failure, humiliation, futile rage, frustration. These de-

* M. Levine, *Psychotherapy in Medical Practice* (New York: The Macmillan Co., 1942).

structive forces are as real as those operating on a physiologic level and may bring about the same results.

The Techniques of Treatment

Operating from the concepts we have formulated it would follow that successful therapy must build up the personality elements which repress or must weaken the threat of the repressed elements. Techniques differ as to their emphasis on one or the other of these components. The so-called supportive treatment relies on a kind of "borrowed" strength which the patient gets from the therapist. The encouragement and understanding offered stimulate and support the patient's ego, giving him additional courage to establish again his former equilibrium. This is the kind of therapy which is intuitively and informally offered by the good friend or the pastor as well as by the physician. People tend to rely on their doctors and unless their confidence is for some reason lost they will accept his guidance as stimulus to activity and courage in re-establishing self control.

The other element involved, that of weakening the repressed elements which are threatening equilibrium, may be dealt with in various ways. We have observed that much repression is established in early life on the basis of the child's inability to deal frankly with conflicting feelings within himself. He tends to react categorically: to establish a pattern of correct attitudes and to assume that he fits into this pattern, not acknowledging the socially and individually unacceptable feelings which contradict it. As he develops the greater objectivity and self-confidence of adulthood he need no longer react so categorically. The pattern, however, has been established and continues automatically. As ego-unacceptable impulses within himself strive for expression he reacts in ways of panic, not realizing that he now possesses the freedom and strength to be able to acknowledge these impulses without being devastated by them.

Treatment therefore encourages the patient to bring that which is unconscious (repressed) into consciousness where it can be viewed in a relatively mature and realistic way. The patient sees more clearly what it is he fears; he is encouraged to deal with it directly rather than blindly to defend himself against it by his repetitive, inefficient, neurotic symptoms. A man, for example, may have repressed strong oral impulses because he has been conditioned from infancy to feel that he must be strong, independent, and aggressive. His longings for reassurance and protection he covers with a façade of extremely active, perhaps even belligerent and dominating behavior. He operates thus under false pretenses and is vulnerable to disturbance because he must constantly strain to convince the world and himself that he is the kind of person he thinks he must be. Any experience, therefore, which strengthens his repressed dependency needs threatens him. Likewise, any experience which weakens the ability of his ego to keep these needs under control threatens him.

At such a time of crisis a man may react in various more or less violent ways, but one type of reaction which brings him to the general physician is the development of illness. The long continued strain disorganizes his physiologic equilibrium. Once symptoms of illness have developed they tend to become chronic because in a neurotic way they provide a resolution of the difficulty. He is ill; therefore he may accept a dependent attitude without stigma.

Treatment of such a person by his physician should be supportive and encouraging but should aim toward an objective acknowledgment of his repressed longings for a more passive, less demanding life. He should learn to think of this longing not as good or bad but as a fact, a part of his functioning, a cause-and-effect phenomenon. If he can accept this frank evaluation of himself he can go on from there in therapy to understand the personality conflicts involved and to find a more mature way of handling them.

Not every patient is able to do this, however, and in some cases the therapist will be most successful if he will recommend a different way of life for "medical" reasons rather than on the basis of the patient's emotional problems. Sensitive discrimination is important here, because a therapist may do much harm by trying to force insight in one who is incapable of it. Such attempts only strengthen defense and denial, or they may precipitate more severe symptoms.

Psychiatric treatment proceeds as a kind of gradual uncovering process. First the symptoms are revealed as expressing emotional disturbance, then this disturbance is seen as a manifestation of conflicting forces, the origin and meaning of which may then be explored.

A young woman comes in with anxiety expressed in dizzy feelings. The relationship of the dizziness and the anxiety soon becomes clear, after which the anxiety is more freely verbalized and takes the form of fear of "losing control—of going crazy." The origins of the fear go back to a tonsillectomy in childhood. The operation had been very frightening and the patient remembers that following it she no longer had the violent temper outbursts of earlier years, but became relatively docile and shy. This led to talk of her early sense of frustration, the result of inconsistently loving and brutal attitudes on the part of the parents. Her ambivalent struggles with her parents had precipitated the tantrums and created in her a deep sense of guilt. In her confusion she then responded to the surgery as to a terrible punishment, with repression of "badness." In later years anything which tended to stimulate her anger or arouse her guilt brought forth not an outburst of rage but a "dizzy spell" as evidence of her fear of her own violence.

These two patients present problems typical of those seen every day by the general physician. He attempts to help them by extending a supportive but objective interest and by guiding them gradually to develop as much insight as they can tolerate toward the origin and nature of their maladjustment.

Such therapy takes time, even when it is conducted in a relatively simple way—but then any method of treating neurotic patients is time consuming, and the physician who evades the real issues and attempts to use strictly medical techniques on them may find them haunting his office for years, going from one symptom or complaint to another as their distress is unrelieved. Some thoughtful, not too hurried consideration at the onset of the difficulty will in many cases break up a tendency to symptom formation and enable the patient to re-establish his former equilibrium.

A physician's success in dealing with the emotional problems of his patients may be considerably favored if he makes use of community resources. Social work groups, when available, are particularly valuable in this respect. Often family problems are closely related to the difficulties of the patient, and other family members are involved. Lack of satisfactory outlets in work or recreation, uncongenial community attitudes, incorrect school placement, or an unsuitable type of vocation all contribute to maladjustment. Whatever the deeper nature of the patient's neurosis may be, his immediate environment is of importance in determining the degree of ego strength which he can utilize in overcoming it. Energies which have become introverted and fixed in symptoms may be stimulated by a more challenging external situation. If this challenge can be followed up to an active and gratifying participation in the affairs of the world the result is good. The ego gains strength through identification with other people in constructive living.

Any individual who attempts to live within himself is vulnerable. The emotionally disturbed person tends to do this, as though to find safety in isolation. Fearing failure, he does not act; fearing rejection, he withholds love; fearing destruction, he lives within a narrow and rigidly controlled pattern. This, however, defeats his own purpose because in such an isolated state—himself against the world—he is terribly aware of his own weakness. If, therefore, he can be encouraged toward outgoing participation he will benefit from it.

The difficulty is that so many people see no opportunities or stimuli for constructive activities. They spend their days in work which is uninteresting to them—perhaps without ever thinking about it or recognizing that they might be happier or more efficient doing something else. This is often true of the housewife. A fair proportion of women are dissatisfied with what they consider to be the restricted role of homemaker. The dissatisfaction may go deeply into a resistance against femininity, or it may be a more simple, realistic feeling of lack of significant goals. Urban apartment house living makes few demands on the woman for efficiency and initiative, especially if she does not have small children. Even the well-adjusted woman becomes restless under these circumstances. If in addition she has a strong sense of inadequacy or is unable to enjoy her wife-and-mother role, the restricted situation emphasizes her difficulties. She needs encouragement to talk frankly of these dissatisfactions and then to make some changes in the direction of occupation outside the home. It is when the doctor has diagnosed a situation of this kind that he may find it helpful to turn the problem over to a social worker. The well-trained worker will not only be able to give advice as to practical vocational possibilities but also may work psychotherapeutically with the patient in the process of readjustment.

Similar circumstances of incompatibility between vocational pursuits and individual interests are of frequent occurrence. The man who is employed by his father for whom he harbors strong but unexpressed resentments, the boy or girl who is being forced by family pressure into a college course for which he is poorly suited, are familiar examples.

Psychiatric treatment by the general physician therefore has first the diagnostic task of evaluating physiologic versus emotional elements in illness and presenting the diagnosis to the patient in such a way as to give him some awareness of the meaning of his disorder without frightening or antagonizing him. Correlated with this task is the supportive, encouraging function of the doctor from which the patient gains confidence and by which he is directed toward a more active, objective attitude toward his emotional problems. We have regarded this supportiveness as contributing to ego strength, thus favoring the patient's re-establishment of equilibrium.

If therapy is to accomplish any more fundamental changes than this it must also be aimed toward uncovering the nature of the repressed conflicts which are at the basis of the illness, making the patient aware of these ideas and feelings so that he can deal consciously and frankly with them instead of fighting them blindly.

The Role of the Psychiatrist

This "uncovering" aspect of treatment presents difficulties for the general physician or for any therapist not intensively trained in psychodynamics. When this approach to a patient's problem seems to be of fundamental importance, then the patient should if possible be referred to a psychiatrist.

The contrast between an "uncovering" approach to a neurotic problem and the approach made by the "supportive" therapist might best be understood by example. A young woman came to her gynecologist with the complaint that she was unable to conceive though she desperately wanted a child. She told him of her habit of taking daily temperature readings to determine the time of ovulation and her insistence on repeated intercourse with her husband at that period, though she admitted to being frigid and rejecting him at other times. She talked volubly of her love for children and her wish to have a large family. The doctor's initial treatment of her was an approving acceptance of her "maternal instincts" and a conscientious attempt to enable her to conceive. He in this way supported her idea of what she wanted to be and encouraged her toward attainment of her goal, ignoring and thus helping her to ignore the fact that her compulsiveness and her frigidity were suggestive of emotional disequilibrium.

Such an approach might in some cases suffice to enable the woman to function, though not too satisfactorily, in the role she wants to establish for herself. In many cases, however, the results of such an acceptance at face value are tragic because the doctor's approval of her presentation of herself makes it even more difficult for the woman to face her real problem. In this particular instance the doctor became aware of the frantic and overanxious attitudes of his patient and referred her to a psychiatrist.

The psychiatrist's orientation gives him an awareness that symptoms often serve to conceal or overcompensate for attitudes and trends which the patient cannot consciously acknowledge. He realizes, therefore, that the woman's exaggerated feelings are suggestive of negative impulses within her which she is violently denying. His task becomes that of encouraging her to talk freely about herself so that he is made aware of the nature of the underlying motivations. In this case it soon became clear that this was a woman who had developed a strong sense of duty and "the fitness of things" which determined her behavior. She had been a "tomboy," closely related to her father whom she tried to please in every way, and remote from her cold mother. Adolescence had been a difficult period for her because she found it hard to share the interests of other girls of that age. She forced herself to dress according to the accepted mode and to go out with boys, though she disliked feminine clothes and was repulsed by the boys' love-making. She had several secret crushes on women teachers and older girls. After college she did not become interested in any particular vocation but worked successfully at several jobs. She was married at twenty-five to a highly eligible man favored by her family "because it seemed to be the thing to do." She admired her husband and they had many common interests so that they got along fairly well in spite of her sexual frigidity. After several years of marriage without serious consideration of pregnancy she decided that it was time to have a baby. "All my friends were having babies." Shortly before this time she had become involved in a friendship with another woman about whom her feelings were very intense. There had been no overt homosexuality, but the patient realized that this relationship was too important to her. She did not face its implications but instead became greatly concerned with her plan to have a child. She said, "If I had a child I would have something to live for; my life would have meaning." Yet her dreams of this period reflected much anxiety and hostility about pregnancy and childbirth.

In a situation of this kind the psychiatrist must evaluate the capacity of the ego to deal with its deeper motivations. Can the woman accept the facts of her homosexual orientation and concentrate on an analysis of these facts, recognizing that for the present at least pregnancy would create serious problems for her, or would this evaluation, by tearing down her neurotic defense, precipitate a serious depression or suicide?

If such a patient comes willingly to a psychiatrist, thus acknowledging an emotional conflict, the chances are that she will be able gradually to look more frankly at herself. She will analyze first the immediate problem and renounce her attempt to solve by denial, then she will explore the reasons for her rejection of femininity. She comes to see that the strivings within her which she has defended against with blind shame and terror are understandable as logical results of her life experience. She relives the ambivalent and confused childhood relationships, projecting as she does so many of the early feelings onto the therapist who accepts and interprets them objectively. Sometimes the result is a process of maturation which enables the patient to feel secure in an adult, heterosexual role. This is the desired goal of therapy. Sometimes, however, the inhibitions are so strongly and so early established that this cannot be accomplished and a compromise is reached. The patient is encouraged to accept herself as she is. A woman like this would in such a case give up the idea of having children and would direct her energies toward the more active, outgoing activities which she could enjoy once she feels less bound by the pattern of conventional feminine behavior.

Resolving the Neurotic Resistance

The "depth" or "uncovering" type of psychotherapy follows for the most part the aims and techniques originated by Sigmund Freud, though with a good many modifications and variations in emphasis. Its aim is to make the patient aware of the nature of his neurotic defenses and to enable him to dispense with them, substituting for them more adult, realistic, and flexible attitudes. This is accomplished by the attainment of an insight which is not only an intellectual understanding but also a *feeling* of the struggle between repressed and repressive forces. Such insight cannot be developed by logical interpretation alone. It is to a large extent the product of the relationship between patient and doctor. In this relationship the patient tends to relive his battles with the world and particularly with the parents. He vacillates between recognizing the therapist as a supportive, non-threatening person and, on the other hand, reacting toward him as an authoritative figure robbing him of the defenses he has built up against such figures. "Cure" means a relinquishment of his rebellion against external forces which at one time were very confusing and frightening to him. This relinquishment is not easily accomplished even though the patient consciously desires it. Resistance shows itself in obscure ways. The patient may begin to miss appointments, or may find himself extremely busy and suggest cutting down the hours. He may develop sudden resentment of the therapist; may insist that he has nothing more to talk about;

he may even concentrate on physical symptoms and minimize the psychiatric problem or decide that he cannot afford to go on with it. In a resistant phase a patient may even lose his symptoms and insist that he is cured though the psychiatrist knows he has not yet made the fundamental changes on which satisfactory improvement must be based. The task of analytic therapy becomes, therefore, to a large extent that of analyzing the patient's resistance against getting well and helping him to give it up.

This might be clarified if we think again of the patient previously described. As her therapy begins she will indicate first, consciously, an unwillingness to see herself, not as a woman desiring the fulfillment of her feminine role in motherhood, but rather as a woman afraid and resentful of her femininity and denying her fears by her attempts to conceive. However, if she is willing to accept psychiatric help at all she will soon accept, intellectually, these facts about herself. Then her struggle has just begun. She has allied her conscious ego with the therapist in peeling off the first layer: the pretense. Now she must recognize the homosexual orientation as itself a neurotic defense established early in life when her possessive attachment to her father and competitiveness with her mother aroused conflicting feelings.

Representation of this infantile conflict in a homosexual way does not have the same significance in every case. Sometimes it expresses an attempt at close relationship with the parent of opposite sex through a kind of identification with that parent; or it may be a protection against erotic feelings in such an identification. The girl is safer with her father in a "man to man" relationship and at the same time wins his favor by following the masculine pattern he admires. A boy, likewise, may identify with his mother to establish such a close and secure rapport with her, assuming feminine attitudes.

A different process having the same result is that in which the boy's or girl's homosexual attitudes represent an attempt to win the parent of the same sex. The boy competes as a female with his mother to win his father's love; the girl's masculinity is an attempt to replace her father in relation to the mother. This "inverted" sexuality manifesting itself at an early age is usually of more serious significance than that which represents a defense against heterosexual anxiety.

Problems such as these, then, underlie the personality deviation of our patient and must be explored if she is to be "cured." The primitive thoughts and feelings of early childhood which are re-activated are expressed more or less directly in the relationship with the doctor. He as a more objective and benign parent figure can interpret them and work toward a revaluation.

The Phenomenon of Transference

The tendency of a patient in intensive therapy to re-activate his conflictual strivings in his relationship with his therapist creates the phenomenon known as transference. Emotionally charged ideas and attitudes which have formerly been more or less completely repressed now manifest themselves consciously and are to some extent "transferred" to the therapist. The fears and hostilities and longings for parents or other intimate associates which the patient has never heretofore been able to deal with frankly and realistically now express themselves as the repressive barriers are let down. And it is easy to see that these strong feelings would become involved with the person to whom they are being directed. The doctor's own personality plays little part in this. He as the protective and directive figure finds himself alternately mother and father, lover and enemy, suspected and trusted. He accepts his various roles but does not himself become emotionally tangled in them, retaining the objectivity necessary to be able to interpret to the patient and encourage him in his attempts to arrive at a realistic integration of the inner turmoil.

A successful working through of the transference is the basis for a good psychoanalysis. It is not, however, a necessary part of all psychotherapeutic procedures and is often contraindicated. Many patients respond best to a therapeutic relationship which does not stir up the old conflicts but instead utilizes the influence of the doctor in his own character, so to speak. The patient is strengthened by having the help of a person who understands his problems and who represents to him more adult ways of dealing with them.

These two aspects of the patient-doctor relationship are not sharply separated and probably both to some extent exist in every prolonged therapeutic undertaking. It is a matter of careful discrimination on the part of the psychiatrist to place the emphasis correctly, to decide when one or the other type of relationship should be encouraged, and in some cases to alternate them according to the patient's need.

Probing the Unconscious: Free Association

The techniques of psychoanalysis are determined by the need for the greatest possible degree of spontaneity of expression on the part of the patient. This is not easily achieved in a face-to-face conversation. As one sits and talks to another person he tends to present his situation in a logical, chronological manner, selecting facts which seem to be significant or disturbing. He expects a response (whether verbally or in facial expression) from his listener, and tends to say what he believes would be of interest. Even when one is a patient talking to a doctor and is therefore attempting to give a complete story he still is handicapped by the formality of this situation. Therefore the method first suggested by Freud, of having the patient lie on a couch, not directly viewing the doctor, is utilized in most cases. The patient is further instructed to try to say everything that comes to mind, verbalizing his thoughts without censorship and with as much objectivity as possible. This free-association technique is in itself of therapeutic value, overcoming some of the anxious tension related to self-expression. It is not an easy procedure, however, and is seldom if ever completely achieved at all times by any patient.

Probing the Unconscious: Dream Analysis

The other important contribution to psychiatric technique made by Freud is the emphasis on systematic interpretation of dreams. He has called them the "royal road to the unconscious," and they are indeed of great value as concise, dramatic revelations of the struggles going on below the level of conscious awareness. This could perhaps be best demonstrated by an example.

A man came for psychiatric help giving two reasons for needing that help. He was acutely disturbed by having learned that his wife was unfaithful to him and felt the need of working out some way of dealing with this emotional disturbance. He said, however, that even more he wanted to overcome a character disorder which all his life had expressed itself in a self-depreciatory attitude, a lack of confidence and aggressiveness.

Two of the first dreams after beginning psychoanalysis he related as follows: "I was fishing, with several companions. We all pulled in fish, but I was afraid of mine and gave it away." "I went into a restaurant and sat beside a big man at a counter. He was eating steak. I wanted steak too but instead ordered ice cream." (He disliked ice cream —remembered his mother always fed it to him when he was sick in childhood.)

Later, as the meaning of his fear of his own masculine aggressiveness was being revealed, he showed signs of resistance. (For example, he forgot appointments, expressed resentment of the doctor, seldom remembered his dreams.) At this time he dreamed: "I was bound hand and foot, unable to move a muscle. I thought, 'This is better. If I don't try I can't fail.'" About this time also he dreamed: "I threw objects [intimately associated with his wife] out the window. I was glad to be rid of them."

A few months later he was showing progress in self-confidence and self-expression. He dreamed then: "I had been bound and was to be burned at the stake. The bandages were afire. But I broke loose and ran, surprised at my strength, and feeling that I could escape." Also: "I was viewing a landscape. In the foreground was a small garden; stretching off on all sides were lands grown to weeds. I thought, 'This is all mine—this huge, untended garden I can cultivate.'"

These dreams are somewhat more simple and transparent than most, but they illustrate the qualities of all dreams: condensation and symbolic expression that reveal dramatically the nucleus of the patient's neurotic conflict. The interpretation here is obvious; in more obscure dreams it can be arrived at only on the basis of the patient's thought associations with the dream elements.

The greatest value of dreams is not the enlightenment which they give the therapist but the insight which the patient derives from them. They are his own product, and as he realizes their implications he becomes directly aware of the nature of his functioning, knows by experience what his conflicts are and how he is dealing with them. It is important, therefore, that the psychiatrist's interpretations never go too far beyond the dreamer's capacity for acceptance. They may surprise and shock him but if they are too completely ego-inacceptable the interpretations may strengthen the patient's defenses against his own unconscious strivings and re-activate the neurosis, at least temporarily. The problem here is the same one we have observed before: that of presenting insight only as the patient is capable of accepting and dealing with it.

The Multiple Approach

A survey such as this of the problems of psychiatric treatment leaves one with seemingly paradoxical conclusions. We recognize that psychiatric disorders are far too widespread and diffuse to be treated with numerical effectiveness only by the small group of trained psychiatrists available for such treatment. On the other hand, we recognize that intensive exploration of the psyche requires a kind of fine discrimination which must be the product of years of study and experience.

The solution which is gradually being evolved is in the direction of greater emphasis on prevention of serious emotional difficulties and early recognition of these difficulties when they do develop. Such a program stresses the importance of better understanding of the emotional life of the child. It works also to encourage frank and unembarrassed attitudes toward neurotic or psychotic symptoms. More clearly defined relationships are being established among general physicians, psychiatrists, psychologists, social workers, and other "auxiliary" treatment groups. All this should in time make available, in every community, resources for the diagnosis and simple supportive therapy which in many cases can prevent later severe psychopathology.

Suggestions for Further Reading

SUGGESTIONS FOR FURTHER READING

GROWTH AND CHARACTER DEVELOPMENT

ALDRICH, C. A. and MARY M. *Babies Are Human Beings.* New York: The Macmillan Co., 1938.

BENEDEK, T. *Psychosexual Functions in Women.* New York: The Ronald Press Co., 1952.

BENEDICT, RUTH. *Patterns of Culture.* Boston: Houghton Mifflin Co., 1934.

BETTELHEIM, B. *Love Is Not Enough.* Glencoe, Ill.: Free Press, 1950.

BURLINGAME, DOROTHY. *Twins.* New York: International University Press, 1952.

CAVAN, R. S., et al. *Personal Adjustment in Old Age.* Chicago: Science Research Associates, 1949.

Community Services for Older People (Wieboldt Foundation Project). Chicago: Wilcox & Follett Co., 1952.

CLIFTON, E., and HOLLIS, F. (eds.). *Child Therapy—A Casework Symposium.* New York: Family Service Association of America, 1948.

DEUTSCH, HELENE. *Psychology of Women.* Vols. I and II. New York: Grune & Stratton, Inc., 1944–45.

ENGLISH, O. S., and PEARSON, G. H. *Emotional Problems of Living.* New York: W. W. Norton & Co., Inc., 1945.

FLUGEL, J. C. *Men and Their Motives.* New York: International University Press, 1947.

———. *The Psychoanalytical Study of the Family.* London: Hogarth Press, Ltd., 1952.

FOSDICK, H. E. *On Being a Real Person.* New York: Harper & Bros., 1943.

GESELL, A. *Infant and Child in the Culture of Today.* New York: Harper & Bros., 1943.

GESELL, A., et al. *The First Five Years of Life.* New York: Harper & Bros., 1940.

———. *The Child from Five to Ten.* New York: Harper & Bros., 1946.

GILBERT, J. G. *Understanding Old Age.* New York: The Ronald Press Co., 1952.

HUNT, J. M. (ed.). *Personality and the Behavior Disorders.* New York: The Ronald Press Co., 1949.

JOHNSON, W. M. *The Years After Fifty.* New York: McGraw-Hill Book Co., Inc., 1947.

JOSSELYN, I. *The Adolescent and His World.* New York: Family Service Association, 1952.

———. *The Psychosocial Development of Children.* New York: Family Service Association, 1948.

Linton, Ralph. *The Cultural Background of Personality.* New York: Appleton-Century-Crofts, Inc., 1945.

Malinowski, B. *Crime and Custom in Savage Society.* New York: Harcourt, Brace & Co., 1926.

Mead, Margaret. *Male and Female.* New York: William Morrow & Co., 1949.

———. *Sex and Temperament in Three Primitive Societies.* New York: New American Library, 1950.

Menninger, K. A. *Love Against Hate.* New York: Harcourt, Brace & Co., 1942.

Moodie, W. *The Doctor and the Difficult Child.* New York: Commonwealth Fund, 1947.

Mullahy, Patrick. *A Study of Interpersonal Relations.* New York: Hermitage Press, Inc., 1949.

Overstreet, H. A. *The Mature Mind.* New York: W. W. Norton & Co., Inc., 1951.

Piaget, Jean. *The Child's Conception of the World.* New York: Harcourt, Brace & Co., 1929.

———. *The Origins of Intelligence in Children.* New York: International University Press, 1952.

Redl, Fritz, and Wineman, D. *Children Who Hate.* Glencoe, Ill.: Free Press, 1951.

Ribble, M. *The Rights of Infants.* New York: Columbia University Press, 1932.

Robinson, H. M. *Why Pupils Fail in Reading.* Chicago: University of Chicago Press, 1946.

Ross, H., and Johnson, A. *Psychiatric Interpretation of the Growth Process.* New York: Family Service Association, 1949.

Saul, L. J. *Emotional Maturity.* Philadelphia: J. B. Lippincott Co., 1947.

Thom, D. A. *Everyday Problems of the Everyday Child.* New York: Appleton-Century-Crofts, Inc., 1942.

THE PATHOLOGICAL STATES

Bradley, Charles. *Schizophrenia in Childhood.* New York: The Macmillan Co., 1942.

Dayton, N. A. *New Facts on Mental Disorders.* Springfield, Ill.: Charles C. Thomas, 1940.

Deutsch, A. *The Mentally Ill in America.* New York: Columbia University Press, 1949.

Freud, S. *Collected Papers,* Vols. I, II, III, IV. London: Hogarth Press, 1925.

———. *The Problem of Anxiety.* New York: W. W. Norton & Co., Inc., 1936.

———. *The Ego and the Mechanism of Defense.* London: Hogarth Press, 1937.

MASLOW, A. H., and MITTLEMANN, B. *Principles of Abnormal Psychology*. New York: Harper & Bros., 1951.
RICHARDSON, H. B. *Patients Have Families*. New York: Commonwealth Fund, 1945.
STERN, E. M. *Mental Illness—A Guide for the Family*. New York: Commonwealth Fund, 1945.
WHITE, ROBT. W. *The Abnormal Personality*. New York: The Ronald Press Co., 1948.

SOCIAL AND RELIGIOUS CONTRIBUTIONS TO MENTAL HEALTH

AUSCHER, RUTH N. (ed.). *The Family—Its Function and Destiny*. New York: Harper & Bros., 1949.
BRUNO, FRANK J. *Trends in Social Work*. New York: Columbia University Press, 1948.
CURRAN, C. A. *Personality Factors in Counseling*. New York: Grune & Stratton, Inc., 1945.
DAVIDSON, H. A. *Forensic Psychiatry*. New York: The Ronald Press Co., 1952.
FARIS, R. E. L. *Social Psychology*. New York: The Ronald Press Co., 1952.
FENTON, N. *Mental Hygiene in School Practice*. Stanford: Stanford University Press, 1943.
FRENCH, L. M. *Psychiatric Social Work*. New York: Commonwealth Fund, 1940.
FREUD, ANNA, et al. *Psychoanalysis for Teachers and Parents*. New York: Emerson Books, Inc., 1935.
FROMM, E. *Psychoanalysis and Religion*. New Haven: Yale University Press, 1950.
GLUECK, S. *Crime and Correction*. Cambridge, Mass.: Addison-Wesley Press, Inc., 1952.
GLUECK, S. and E. T. *500 Criminal Careers*. New York: Alfred A. Knopf, Inc., 1930.
———. *Preventing Crime*. New York: McGraw-Hill Book Co., Inc., 1936.
———. *Unraveling Juvenile Delinquency*. New York: Commonwealth Fund, 1950.
HAMILTON, G. *Theory and Practice of Social Case Work*. (2d ed.). New York: Columbia University Press, 1951.
HEALY, W., and BRONNER, AUGUSTA. *New Light on Delinquency and Its Treatment*. New Haven: Yale University Press, 1947.
JAMES, W. *The Varieties of Religious Experience*. New York: Random House, Inc., 1902.
KARDINER, ABRAM. *The Individual and His Society*. New York: Columbia University Press, 1946.
———. *The Psychological Frontiers of Society*. New York: Columbia University Press, 1945.

Kasius, Cora (ed.). *A Comparison of Diagnostic and Functional Casework Concepts.* New York: Family Service Association, 1950.

Lee, Porter R., and Kenworthy, Marian. *Mental Hygiene and Social Work.* New York: Commonwealth Fund, 1929.

Levy, John, and Munroe, Ruth. *The Happy Family.* New York: Alfred A. Knopf, Inc., 1945.

Reik, T. *The Secret Self.* New York: Farrar, Straus & Co., Inc., 1952.

Redl, F., and Wattenberg, W. *Mental Health in Teaching.* New York: Harcourt, Brace & Co., 1951.

Rennie, T., and Woodward, L. *Mental Health in Modern Society.* New York: Commonwealth Fund, 1948.

Watson, R. I. *The Clinical Method in Psychology.* New York: Harper & Bros., 1951.

PSYCHIATRY AND PSYCHOANALYSIS:
AIMS AND TECHNIQUES

Alexander, F. and Ross, H. *Dynamic Psychiatry.* Chicago: University of Chicago Press, 1952.

Alexander, F. and French, T. M. *Psychoanalytic Therapy.* New York: The Ronald Press Co., 1946.

———. *Studies in Psychosomatic Medicine—An Approach to the Cause and Treatment of Vegetative Disturbances.* New York: The Ronald Press Co., 1948.

Brill, A. A. *Freud's Contribution to Psychiatry.* New York: W. W. Norton & Co., Inc., 1944.

Fenichel, Otto. *The Psychoanalytic Theory of Neurosis.* New York: W. W. Norton Co., Inc., 1945.

Ferenczi, S. *Theory and Teaching of Psychoanalysis.* London: Hogarth Press, Ltd., 1950.

Freud, S. *An Outline of Psychoanalysis* (translation). New York: W. W. Norton & Co., Inc., 1949.

———. *The Interpretation of Dreams, in The Basic Writings of Sigmund Freud.* New York: Random House, 1938.

Fromm-Reichman, F. *Principles of Intensive Psychotherapy.* Chicago: University of Chicago Press, 1950.

Grinker, R. R. *Psychosomatic Research.* New York: W. W. Norton & Co., 1953.

Group for Advancement of Psychiatry Reports. Topeka, Kansas: G. A. P. Publishing Office, 1952.

Hendrick, Ives. *Facts and Theories of Psychoanalysis.* New York: Alfred A. Knopf, Inc., 1946.

Hinsey, L. E. *Understandable Psychiatry.* New York: The Macmillan Co., 1949.

Horney, Karen. *Are You Considering Psychoanalysis.* New York: W. W. Norton & Co., Inc., 1946.

Kubie, L. S. *Practical and Theoretical Aspects of Psychoanalysis.* New York: International University Press, 1950.

MENNINGER, W. C. *Psychiatry in a Troubled World*. New York: The Macmillan Co., 1948.
MENNINGER, W. C., and LEAF, MUNRO. *You and Psychiatry*. New York: Charles Scribner's Sons, 1948.
PRESTON, G. H. *Psychiatry for the Curious*. New York: Farrar and Rinehart, Inc., 1940.
ROHEIM, G. *Psychoanalysis and the Social Sciences*. New York: International Universities Press, 1947.
SCHILDER, P. *Psychotherapy*. New York: W. W. Norton & Co., Inc., 1951.
THOMPSON, C., and MULLAHY, P. *Psychoanalysis—Evolution and Development*. New York: Hermitage Press, Inc., 1951.

Index

Adaptation
  capacity for, 6
  constructive, 54
  difficulties of, 5
  by distortion and denial, 110 ff.
  by ego, 53
  first life period, 11
  limiting factor of, 48
  patterns of, 5
  problems of, 3, 7
  tool of, 89
  unrealistic, 73
  within the peer group (childhood), 20–27
Adaptive tasks, 4
Addictions, 101 ff.
Adequacy and overflow, 36–44
Adolescence, 4, 20, 26, 28–45, 55
Adolescent revolt, 29
Advertising writer, 39
Aggression, 22, 66, 80, 105, 142
Alcoholic neurosis, 101 ff.
Alcoholics Anonymous, 103
Alcoholism, 101 ff., 147, 149
Alexander, F., 78
Allergies, 83
Ambivalence, 14, 55, 88, 118
Amentia, 144 ff.
Anal character, 97
Anorexia nervosa, 82
Antisocial behavior, 104
Antisocial character, 56–58
Anxieties
  about attachments to parents, 16
  about castration, 16, 101
  about dirt, 97
  about elimination, 10
  disorganization by, 79
  early development of, 7
  in illness, 81
  meaning of, 70, 78 ff.
  of later life, 50
  of military service, 80
  overwhelming, 80
  resulting from rejection, 18
Anxiety hysteria, 89, 90, 93
Anxiety state, 80, 91, 92, 154
Arteriosclerosis, 47, 147, 149
Arthritis, 47, 82
Artist, 39, 40, 56
Asthma, 83
Attitudes
  of acceptance, 21, 22
  of adolescent, 32
  adult, 36
  affectionate, dependent, 14
  aggressive, 24
  ambivalent, 118
  arrogant, 61
  based on love, 15
  change during involution, 45
  of children, 22
  conformity of, 9
  constructive, 112
  cultural, 65
  destructive, 35
  discouraged, 7
  emotional, 26, 29
  greedy, 10, 118
  hostile, 137
  in illness, 81
  of inferiority, 16, 33
  internalization of, 57
  mature, 39, 40
  moral, 105
  of parents, 15, 53

Attitudes (*Continued*)
  of paranoiac, 142
  reflect experience, 19
  suppressed, 87
  toward teachers, 165
  unacceptable, 88
  withdrawn, 32
  workers', 40
Aurelius, Marcus, 36

Bedwetting, 64, 172
Biological processes, influence of, 62
Bleuler, Eugen, 122, 124
Blood pressure, 76, 79, 82
Brain disease, 128, 131, 137, 143 ff.
Business, 58

Cancer, 48, 128
Cannon, W. B., 79
Catatonic stupor, 130
Character
  alteration of, 149
  anal, 97
  antisocial, 56–58
  compulsive traits of, 76
  defensive, 61
  definition of, 52
  delinquent, 57, 76
  feminine, 66
  formation, 34, 52–70, 73
  masculine traits, 65
  neurotic, 74
  oral, 63, 102
  paranoid, 58, 59
  patterns, 32, 54, 60
  traits, 10, 15, 54, 63
  withdrawn, 127
Charcot, J. M., 94
Child guidance clinic, 156
Childhood
  early, 12–19
  later, 20–27
Children
  brain damaged, 145
  defiant, 33
  dependence on parents, 12
  family relationships of, 16
  favoritism among, 18
  institutionalized, 8
  point of view of, 25
  position among siblings, 17
  relative abilities of, 18
  resolution of conflicts of, 16
  socialization of, 21
  suffering for causes, 25
Christ, 169
Christian religion, 69
Church, 167, 170
"Classical" neuroses, 85
Claustrophobia, 90
Comfort seeking, 4, 13
Compensations, 60, 61
Compulsive-obsessive neurosis, 96–99
Compulsiveness, 37, 74, 76
Conformity, 25, 60, 64, 96
Confucius, 169
Constipation, 10, 64
Constitutional factors, 5, 30, 47, 49, 70, 76, 105, 116, 128, 136, 144
Conversion, 85, 94
Conversion hysteria, 92, 93, 95, 138
Conversion neurosis, 96
Conversion state, 93, 96
Convulsive state, 95
Cretinism, 146
Criminal, 106
Cultural emphasis, 15, 69, 141, 149
Cultural traditions, 33, 62, 65

Daydreamer, 54, 55, 57, 58
Daydreams, 33, 54
Defense mechanisms, 47
Delinquency rate, 57
Delinquent, 54, 57, 58, 104
Delirium, 147, 148
Delusions of persecution, 111, 130, 137 ff.
Demagogues, 59
Dementia, 147, 148
Dementia praecox, 122
Depression, 107 ff., 119
Diabetes, 47

INDEX

Diarrhea, 77, 80
Dictator, 68
Digestion, 77
Disorientation to time and place, 147
Distortion and denial, 111
Domination, 17
Dostoyevsky, Fyodor, 153
Dream analysis, 189
Dreamer, 54–56
Dreams, 101, 126, 143, 190
Drug poisoning, 147
Drugs, 104
Dunbar, F., 78

Ego, 52, 53, 54, 60–62, 79, 86, 89, 92, 100, 104, 106, 111, 116 ff., 175
Electric shock treatment, 96, 119
Encephalitis, 146
Environment, 6, 128
Enuresis, 64, 172
Erickson, Erik H., 27
Erythrobia, 90
Exhibitionism, 13, 100, 104
Experience, 6

Fantasy, 55, 56, 60, 98, 111, 119, 123, 124, 127, 129, 131, 135, 142
Federn, Paul, 114
Feeding (of children), 7, 9, 43
Femininity, 15
Free Association; 188
French, T. M., 78
Freud, Sigmund, 52, 185, 189
Friends, 51
Frustration, 14, 55, 119, 145, 149

Gesell, Arnold, 9
Grinker, R. R., 78
Group(s)
  adolescent, 31
  altruistic, 61
  delinquent, 34
  integration, 35
  minority, 23–25
  peer, 20–22, 26
  persecutory tendencies of, 59
  play, 20, 21
  rejection by, 22
  relationships, 28
  therapy, 135

Hallucinations, 126
Hate, 12, 14, 20, 34, 167
Headaches, 76
Health, 47, 49, 84
Hebephrenic schizophrenia, 131
Hemophilia, 128
Heredity, 6, 127
Hippocrates, 93
Hoch, P. H., 119
Homeostasis, 6
Homosexuality, 67, 143, 186
Hospitals, state, population of, 149
Hostility, 13, 14, 22, 34, 35, 42, 88, 89, 96, 99, 105, 117
Housman, A. E., 73
Hypertension, 47
Hypnosis, 94–96
Hypochondria, 174
Hypomanic, 117
Hysteria, 93

Id, 52, 53, 80, 89, 116, 118
Ilg, Ferena, 9
Illegitimacy, 24
Immaturity, 37, 41, 43, 58, 96
Impulse neurosis, 100 ff.
Impulse, unrestrained, 100
Infancy, 3–11
Inhibitions, 102
Insight, 75, 178, 185, 191
Intelligence, 5, 18, 40, 145
Involution, 45–51
Involutional melancholia, 121
Involutional psychosis, 121

James, William, 3
Jealousy, 17
Jewish religious groups, 169
Johnson, Samuel, 52
Judgment, impairment, 148

INDEX

Kalinowsky, L. B., 119
Kleptomania, 100–2, 104
Kraepelin, Emil, 122

Levine, M., 175
Longfellow, H. W., 20
Love, 12–16, 20, 29, 34, 42, 48, 49, 103, 143
Love and hate in childhood, 12–19

McKay, H. D., 57
Manic-depressive psychosis, 111, 115 ff.
Marital discord, 18
Marriage, 34, 43, 67
Martyr, 60
Masculinity, 15, 24
Masturbation, 14, 26, 33
Maturity, 4, 28, 35, 36–44, 49, 58, 63
Maugham, W. Somerset, 61
Melancholia, involutional, 121
Memory impairment, 148
Mental deficiency, 145
Mental hygiene, 155 ff.
Middle age, 46, 47
Migraine, 82
Military service, 80, 127
Minorities, 23, 24, 31, 39, 58, 61, 142
Mongolism, 146
Moral sense, 53, 57, 60
Movies, 41
Mutism, hysterical, 95
Myerson, A., 131

Narcissism, 13, 50, 56
Nationalism, 58
Nausea, 77, 80
Neurosis, 62, 73–76, 98 ff.
  alcoholic, 101 ff.
  "classical," 85
  compulsive-obsessive, 96–99
  conversion, 96
  impulse, 100
  obsessive-compulsive, 85, 98
  somatic, 74, 84, 92

Neurosyphilis, 149
Neurotic depression, 107 ff.
Neurotic disturbance, 81 ff.
Nursery school, 20, 21

Objectivity in evaluating character, 70
Obsession, 97
Obsessive-compulsive neurosis, 85, 98
Old age, 45–51, 149
Omnipotence, 5, 6
Orphan, 24
Oral character, 63, 102, 118
Oral frustration, 10
Oral traits, 83
Organic triad, 148
Overcompensation, 60–64, 68
Overprotection, 17

Paranoia, 62, 111, 137 ff.
Paranoiac, 138 ff.
Paranoid schizophrenia, 130, 139–40
Paranoid states, 137, 140
Paranoid tendencies, 58, 59, 62, 69, 111, 137, 141
Pastor, 167, 176
Pediatrician, 156, 172
Perfectionism, 10, 60, 73
Permissiveness, 7
Phobia, 85, 89, 90, 102
Phobic state, 89 ff.
Physician, 76, 77, 154, 157 ff., 171 ff., 192
Play activities, 41
Politics, 40, 58, 61, 141
Preconscious, 86
Prejudices, 25
Priest, Catholic, 169
Professions, 40
Projection, 18, 137
Projection of blame, 58, 59, 127
Protestant church, 169
Prudery, 60
Psychiatric social work, 162 ff.

INDEX

Psychiatrist
  role of, 182 ff.; training of, 153
Psychiatry in medical curriculum, 158
Psychoanalysis, 170 ff.
Psychoanalyst, training of, 153
Psychodynamics, 113
Psychologist's role, 160 ff., 192
Psychopathic personality, 104 ff.
Psychosis, 62, 103, 107, 110 ff.
  involutional, 121
  manic-depressive, 111, 115 ff.
  paranoid, 62, 111, 137 ff.
  schizophrenic, 62, 111, 114 ff., 132–34
  toxic-exhaustive, 147
Psychosomatic illness, 84
Psychosomatic medicine, 47, 76
Psychotherapy, 170 ff.
Psychotic, 59, 106
Psychotic breakdown, 110 ff., 127
Psychotic depression, 109, 114
Pyromania, 100, 101

Reactive depression, 108
Reality
  adjustments to, 79
  denial of, 123, 127
  evasions of, 74
  of the psychotic, 111
  perceived by ego, 116
  presentation of, 6, 7
Reassurance, need for, 49, 63
Rebellion, 10, 29, 32, 34, 37, 44, 64, 96
Regression, 129, 130
Religion, 141, 167 ff.
Religious ethics, 69
Repression, 86–88, 91, 95, 97, 99, 117, 168, 175
Retirement, 50
Retreat, 73

Salesman, 39, 40
Schizophrenia, 62, 111, 114 ff.
  case studies of, 132–34

Schizophrenic episode, 127
  process, 127
Self-acceptance, problem of, 45–51
Senility, 149
Senn, M. J., 9
Sexual drives, 26, 28
Sexuality "inverted," 187
Shakespeare, William, 8, 12, 110
Shaw, Clifford, 57
Shock treatment, 119, 121, 136
Sibling(s), 13, 14, 17, 18, 24
"Sissy," 23, 24, 66
Social acceptance, 28
Social drinking, 102
Social work, 162, 179
Social worker, 181, 192
Socrates, 75
Somatic neurosis, 74, 84, 92
Spastic colitis, 82
Spitz, Dr. Renee, 8, 9
Split mind, 124
Spock, Benjamin, 9
State hospitals, population of, 149
"Strength of character," 54
Sublimation, 61, 63, 68, 88
Subconscious, 85
Suicide, 120
Superego, 52–57, 80, 88, 89, 99, 102–6, 116 ff.
Superstitions, 98
Suppression, 87
Symbolic symptoms, 74, 85
Syphilis, 146, 147

Teacher, 164 ff.
Television, 41
Theatre, 61
Thyroid extract, treatment with, 146
Toilet training, 7, 9, 10, 43, 64, 96
"Tomboy," 23, 24, 66
"Total Push," 131
Toxic-exhaustive psychosis, 147
Transference, 187 ff.
Traumatic experience, 47

Treatment
  of delirium, 147
  of depressed patient, 119
  problem of, 153 ff.
  psychiatric, 153 ff.
  of schizophrenia, 134
  techniques of, 176 ff.
Tuberculosis, 128

Ulcer, 82, 83
Unconscious, 85, 86, 94, 177, 188

Veterans Administration, 162
Voyeurism, 100

Whitman, Walt, 28
Withdrawn mechanisms, 62
Worker, 39

Yeats, William B., 45

Zilboorg, G., 112